SO-AVX-916

ANTHROPOLOGICAL STUDIES

DAVID H. MAYBURY-LEWIS, Editor

Number 10

The ARCTIC HYSTERIAS
of the North Alaskan Eskimo

EDWARD F. FOULKS

Published by the

AMERICAN ANTHROPOLOGICAL ASSOCIATION
1703 New Hampshire Avenue, N.W.
Washington, D.C. 20009

Contents

DEDICATION

In honor of John Gillin, distinguished anthropologist and former president of the American Anthropological Association, whose contributions in the areas of Latin America, Ethnology, Culture and Personality, Theory and Interdisciplinary cooperation, have advanced the frontiers of anthropology.

The John Gillin Award, established in 1972 by his friends, colleagues, family, and former students has provided for this publication, which exemplifies scientific progress in the understanding of the "Ways of Men."

ACKNOWLEDGMENTS

The author wishes to express appreciation to the authors and publishers for permission to quote from the following material:

Gussow, Z.
  1960 Pibloktok Hysteria among the Polar Eskimos. *In* Psychoanalytic Study of Society. W. Muensterberger, Ed. New York: International Universities Press, pp 205, 206, 207, 209.
Heller, C. and E. Scott
  1961 The Alaska Dietary Survey 1956-1961. Public Health Service Publication No. 999-AH-2, Washington, D.C., pp 47, 49, 50, 61.
MacMillan, D.
  n.d. Peary's Expedition through Greenland. Prints (North Pole Expedition). The American Museum of Natural History.
Nelson, R.
  1969 Hunters of the Northern Ice. Chicago, Illinois: University of Chicago Press, pp 386-387.
Spencer, R.
  1959 The North Alaskan Eskimo. Bureau of American Ethnology. Bulletin No. 171, Washington, D.C., pp 318-323.
Wallace, A.F.C.
  1960 An Interdisciplinary Approach to Mental Disorder Among the Polar Eskimos of Northwest Greenland. Anthropologica N.S. 11(2):1-12.
  1961 Culture and Personality. New York: Random House.
  1961 Mental Health, Biology and Culture. *In* Psychological Anthropology. F. Hsu, Ed. Homewood, Illinois: Dorsey Press.

*When we try to pick
out anything by itself,
We find it hitched
to everything else in
the universe.*

John Muir
Gentle Wilderness, p. 154

Preface

IN 1964, after having finished medical school and an internship, I began a four-year residency program in adult and child psychiatry at the Eastern Pennsylvania Psychiatric Institute. On the day of my arrival I had the opportunity of attending a seminar given by Margaret Mead on Freud's book *Totem and Taboo.* Her discussions broadened my perspective of human nature to include the individual and his personality within the context of his culture and society. Shortly thereafter I became acquainted with Robert Kraus and Anthony Wallace. Robert Kraus, a psychiatrist and graduate student in the Department of Anthropology at the University of Pennsylvania, had long been interested in the relationships between culture and mental disorder. Anthony Wallace had written extensively on the subject of culture and personality, and had published several articles dealing specifically with the Arctic Hysterias. My long lasting contact with both of these men has provided a continuing inspiration in my own work.

Anthony Wallace has long advocated an interdisciplinary approach in understanding the behaviors of individuals in the contexts of their environment and culture. He pointed out that the interface between man's psychology and his environment is to be found in the physiological functioning of his central nervous system. He therefore broadened the perspectives of personality and culture to include interacting cultural, environmental, psychological, and physiological systems.

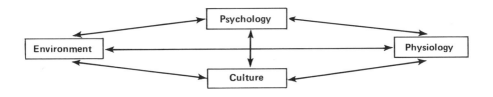

This study begins as I began in 1964 with a perspective of culture and personality studies including the works of Margaret Mead and Anthony Wallace. The ordering of the chapters following continues to reflect quite fortuitously the influences on my own thinking from 1964 to the present. In 1965, I began formal course work in anthropology at the University of Pennsylvania. There Froelich Rainey inspired further interest in the Eskimos, especially those groups living in north Alaska where he had worked for many years. Ruben Reina provided me with an appreciation of the dynamics of cultural systems, and the impact of tradition in shaping the behavior of a people.

In 1966, Dr. Wallace introduced me to Solomon Katz who had published extensively in the area of human biology and had special research interests related to calcium metabolism and mental functioning. Wallace had suggested that deficiencies in calcium among the Eskimos might have been responsible for aberrancies of central nervous system functioning resulting in Arctic Hysteria. He had originally proposed to test this hypothesis in the field among the Thule of northwest Greenland. Dr. Katz and I were invited to collaborate on this study. Preparations for this fieldwork required utilizing methods of traditional medicine which are reflected in the chapters of this study dealing with differential diagnosis, the calcium hypothesis, and central nervous system disorders. I would like to make special mention of my indebtedness to Solomon Katz. Sol has been my teacher, my companion in the field, and my friend. He has involved himself deeply and tirelessly in helping my fieldwork, and in guiding the writing of this book.

For a variety of reasons, fieldwork in Greenland was not possible. Our focus therefore shifted to more accessible regions in Alaska and Canada where the Arctic Hysterias had also been reported. In June, 1969, my wife, my son, and I began our year's study among the Eskimos of North Alaska. I will be forever grateful for the friendship and support offered by many individuals and agencies in Alaska, without which my work would have been impossible. Special gratitude is extended to Jack McCombs of the Department of Health and Welfare; to Carl Koutsky, MD, Director of the Alaska Psychiatric Institute; to Peter Morrison, PhD, Director of the Institute of Arctic Biology; to Fred Milan, PhD, then Director of Eskimo Research under the International Biological Program; to Dr. Max Brewer and the staff of the Naval Arctic Research Laboratory in Barrow, Alaska; and to Richard Lyons, MD, of the Arctic Health Research Institute.

This research was accomplished through support of the Institute of Arctic Biology, the University of Alaska, and through the Human Adaptability Section of the International Biological Program.

I. A Synthetic Approach

THIS IS A STUDY of the Arctic Hysterias, a group of mental disorders which have occurred with some frequency among circumpolar-peoples from pre-contact periods to the present time. The subject may surprise those who consider mental disorders a product of the complexities of modern, overpopulated, socially stratified urban society. However, it is apparent that even in the pristine purity of primitive peoples problems arise that result in mental disorders. Cross-cultural comparisons of mental disorders have recently revealed that no society is entirely free of them. The forms manifested by the mentally disordered, however, do vary according to cultural patterns and particular ecosystems (*Transcultural Psychiatric Research Review* 1956-71).

Many different cultural groups inhabit the circumpolar regions from Lappland across Siberia to Alaska, Canada, and Greenland. Genetic differences among many of these peoples is also correspondingly great, as for example between the Lapp and Eskimo. On the other hand, living in an Arctic environment with its characteristic floral and faunal forms presents a multitude of common problems and potentials for human exploitation. Consequently, contact and borrowing among many of these circumpolar peoples has occurred over thousands of years. Thus despite present differences in historical traditions, in overall cultural forms, and in genetic constitution, there are many cultural items and institutions which retain similar forms and functions over the entire circumpolar region. Even today, the USA, Canada, Denmark, Norway, Sweden, Finland, and USSR in administering the circumpolar regions find an international common bond in the problems of acculturation, education, welfare, health, and mental health presented by the aboriginal peoples of this area.

Among the list of items and institutions common to all circumpolar peoples are the mental disorders generically termed the Arctic Hysterias. This thesis will attempt to establish the historical-traditional relationships of this behavior among peoples of the north in general. Then we will explore in detail its role in the history and culture of the Innuit Eskimo, a people in whom episodes of the Arctic Hysterias have been amply documented since the earliest contact times. Finally, the present day patterns of occurrence among the Innuit of Alaska will be analyzed. This analysis will first consist of an overall incidence study of mental disorders which occurred in Alaskan natives during the year 1968. Then we will focus on the particular factors which are involved in the Arctic Hysterias in north Alaska. These factors include historo-cultural traditions; social organization; arctic environmental and dietary patterns; general health factors as parturition procedures, prenatal morbidity, infant morbidity from infectious disease, otitis media, and central nervous system aberrations; and psychological dynamics. The factors to be considered are great in number and diverse in scope, ranging from biochemical and psychological to the social-cultural. The purpose of this multidimensional exploration will not only be to elucidate the particular causes of the Arctic Hysterias, but more importantly to demonstrate the interactions and summations of these factors as interdependent systems. Detailing and integrating these systems will be the main theme of this volume. The Arctic Hysterias will be the main focus.

THE IDEA OF MULTIPLE CAUSAL PATHWAYS

The theory that mental symptoms are psychologically overdetermined has been well explored in recent years. Overdetermination here means the causation of a specific mental symptom by a variable member of intersecting causal paths. The term is derived from geometry where two intersecting lines overdetermine the point (Moore and Fine 1968:69). This idea has been restricted so far to interacting psychological factors. The hysterical convulsion, for example, may represent at one and the same time the expression of a sexual or aggressive wish, the prohibitions against that wish, the avoidance of anxiety, as well as some secondary psychological gains such as attracting attention, receiving care and concern of others, and in some cases gaining monetary reinforcement in the form of welfare disability payments or damage settlements. In this example, the convulsive symptom depends on the mutual interactions, summations and reinforcements of a variety of psychological forces.

Psychological overdeterminism thus views every mental symptom as immeshed in a dynamic matrix of multiply determined, but mutually dependent intrapsychic forces. The sciences of anthropology and sociology have recently contributed much toward enlarging this perspective. The principal argument of this book is that a piece of behavior or a mental symptom is not only psychologically overdeterminal, but in fact is embedded in a larger network of interacting systems which extend far beyond the individual. They extend to his family, his culture, his biological environment, his society, his place in history, and in the very evolution of the human species. The methods and theoretical approaches used in this book are necessarily interdisciplinary, involving contributions from anthropology, sociology, psychology, psychiatry, psychoanalysis, and human biology. The approach used is essentially synthetic in intent; it seeks to relate interacting factors from a variety of dimensions in order to create a coherent dynamic. This dynamic will represent patterns of interacting forces in an individual's life which have been involved in the aberrant mental functioning manifested in Arctic Hysteria. The model will not pretend to have discovered the causes of mental illness. There are important factors involved in the etiology of mental disorder which are at present unknown. Instead, the advantage of this synthetic model will hopefully be in understanding the complexity of forces which are involved in the symptom-atology, chronicity, and social handling of an individual with a mental disorder.

EARLIER CONTRIBUTIONS TO A SYNTHETIC MODEL OF "PERSONALITY AND CULTURE"

The notion of synthesizing seemingly disparate elements into a coherent whole is of course not new in anthropology. In 1927 Sapir presented one of the first anthropological papers dealing with theories of personality formation within the context of culture (Mandelbaum 1949). Perhaps influenced by Freud's discovery of the "unconscious," Sapir maintained that those automatic, often unconscious organizations of individual behavior which are termed personality were primarily molded by an individual's experience in his cultural milieu. Shortly thereafter, Mead published several psycho-cultural studies, *Coming of Age in Samoa* (1928), *Growing Up in New Guinea* (1930), and *Sex and Temperament in Three Primitive Societies* (1935). Mead felt that the infant, by virtue of its constitution, possessed a basic temperament which culture shaped and molded during the years of growing up. If a child's basic temperament were naturally the same as the ideal set by his society, his personality adjustments would be so much the easier. If a child's basic temperament were slightly antagonistic to the ideal of the society, such as a somewhat active child in a group which demanded passivity, the personality would necessarily make some adjustments toward behaving passively. If, on the other hand, the basic temperament were the antithesis of the society's ideal, and no personality adjustments sufficed to narrow those differences, the individual would suffer the conflicts of this position. Basic to Mead's formula is the notion that a wide range of basic temperament exists in any human group. From this range of temperaments culture establishes an ideal to which most are able to adjust. A few are so extremely different, that adjustment is impossible within their particular cultural context and they suffer accordingly.

Benedict (1934) elaborated this basic notion. She, too, felt that a spectrum of temperamental types potentially existed in all human groups and that the configurations of culture required certain of these types and not others. So integrated and parallel was the mutual influence of psychology and culture that culture itself was conceptualized as sort of a type of "psychology thrown large upon the screen, given gigantic proportions and a long time span" (Benedict 1932:24). In terms of understanding individual psychology, Benedict had added new depth. The individual has a personal history in growing up and adjusting to the requirements of his culture. The requirements of his culture, however, also have a history independent from his. Thus the study of an individual's personality is examined in the context of his cultural heritage. His psychology represents a present day extension of cultural tradition of "gigantic proportion and a long time span." To understand one, the investigator must appreciate the other. In this thesis we will attempt to understand the psychology of certain Eskimos with Arctic Hysteria. In doing so we utilize this historical approach.

PSYCHOANALYTIC THEORY IN "CULTURE AND PERSONALITY"

Formal psychoanalytic theory was applied to culture and personality studies by Kardiner and his co-workers, Sapir, Benedict, Bunzel, Linton, DuBois, and Withers, at Columbia University. They postulated that every society generates a "basic personality structure" in each of its members, which is formed primarily through the influence of child rearing practices, family organization and subsistence patterns. These institutions were considered "primary" and fundamentally stable, unlikely to be interfered with by the vicissitudes of climate or economy (Kardiner 1939:471). Emotional and biological needs unfulfilled by the "primary institutions" were felt to create frustrations and conflicts, which in turn were handled by a shared series of psychological defense systems which were termed "secondary institutions." These institutions included taboo systems, religion, rituals, folktales, group ideology, cognitive orientations to life and death, etc.

The psychoanalytic understanding of mental disorders in the context of a society involved discovering the pathogenic socializing practices which interfered with the normal phases of childhood psychosexual development and resulted in certain neurotic fixations. These neurotic fixations were felt to persist into adult life, where they are manifested as mental disorder. Such neurotic fixations in basic personality have been studied for example by using psychological tests (Billig, Gillin, and Davidson 1947; Katz and Foulks 1969). Mead and Benedict stressed the importance of understanding personality through understanding the history of culture. Kardiner and his group have stressed the importance of understanding personality through understanding the development of that personality. This approach will also be a major consideration of this study.

WHERE DOES BIOLOGY FIT IN?

A major development for a synthetic understanding of personality functioning sprang from the works of Whiting and his co-workers. Using the statistical version of the comparative method perfected by George Murdock's Human Relations Area Files, Whiting (1961) produced statistical cross-cultural indications of a causal chain between child rearing practices, personality variables, and projective systems (secondary institutions). An early example of the approach was his correlation between the length of time during which an infant sleeps with his mother and the occurrence of male initiation rites (Whiting, Kluckhohn, and Anthony 1958). It was felt that this sleeping arrangement intensified Oedipal rivalry between father and son, and that puberty rites provided an institutionalized resolution of the situation. Prolonged contact with mother was also seen as inhibiting appropriate masculine identification with father, which again was provided through the puberty rites, formal initiation into manhood. Quite significantly, Whiting (1964) later found more traits that correlated cross-culturally with prolonged sleeping arrangements between infant and mother and puberty rites. They included prolonged postpartum sexual taboo, prolonged infant nursing, polygyny, patrilocality, tropical climate, and Kwashiorkor (a protein deficiency in infancy often leading to death, but at times rendering an individual mentally disordered and intellectually retarded because of irreversible impairment of the brain). The protein deficiencies in the tropical diet were felt to have placed an adaptive premium on prolonged nursing to maintain the infant's protein intake as long as possible. Interruption of lactation by demands of a second infant was prevented by prolonged postpartum sex taboo while mother nursed. The sex taboo encouraged the presence of a second wife. In this polygynous household the husband slept separately from the infant-mother pair. Polygyny also rendered patrilocality more probable, as the most convenient way to maintain a household. Patrilineality was seen as the natural consequence of patrilocality. In addition to the psychological pressures to resolve the Oedipal situation, young boys in a strongly patrilineal, patrilocal society are subject to intense pressure to assure proper male role identity, thus they are subjected to a severe puberty rite. Here Whiting's correlations and causal chains offer new directions of inquiry in culture and personality studies.

First they demonstrate how biological factors interdigitate with cultural and personality factors to result in a unified, complex field. Mead and Benedict viewed basic personality as a key piece in a puzzle of many interlocking pieces which represented various cultural institutions. The overall picture of the puzzle represented the complex totality of a culture. In addition, they conceptualized such a puzzle as moving and changing through time. At times one piece would change shape, requiring those around it to change their shape accordingly. At other times a piece would be replaced by another piece from the outside, one with the same shape but a different picture, thus distorting the overall original picture. Whiting's work suggests that yet another dimension, the biological, must be included in order to understand the dynamics of this matrix. The biological includes a consideration of the physical external environment which supports and interacts with the cultural system. The biological also includes the physiological internal environment of the human organisms which carry the culture. There is a dynamic interaction between the physical environment and the physiological environment. Both, of course, are essential to the support and overall configuration and picture that is culture. In turn, many aspects of culture represent unique solutions of human adaptation to physical and biological aspects of the environment which might not be met if man had to depend on his basic physiological potentials alone.

Another dimension of the biological to be given consideration in this study is its direct effect on mental functioning. Environmental factors such as climate, diet, and disease, affect not only social institutions, which in turn shape personality, but in many cases impinge directly on the functioning of the human central nervous system, which is the biological substratum of personality itself (see Katz and Foulks 1969).

Wallace called attention to the importance of considering biological factors in any investigation of "personality in culture" by pointing out that:

> With respect to cultural anthropology's participation in the scientific investigation of mental illness the most glaring weakness has been the bland assumption that mental disorder is caused by disorders in social, cultural and psychological processes. This bland assumption in part has been based on failure to consider seriously the fact that the various known organic impairments can and do regularly produce symptomatologies . . . ranging from psychosis to the transient situational reactions. It has also in part been based on neglect of the existing evidence for genetic and biochemical complicity in the development of supposedly "psychogenic" or "functional" psychoses. Since cultural anthropologists generally are consulted by, and read the works of those psychiatrists and psychologists who are committed to the psycho-social tradition, this bias is not corrected from outside the field, but remains to stunt the development of cultural anthropological research in this important area [Wallace 1961:172-173].

Being aware of biological factors in personality functioning has special relevance for the anthropologist since it is precisely those areas of the world which are of greatest anthropological concern which are also likely to harbor pathogenic agents capable of affecting central nervous system functioning. Problems of sanitation, diet, insect vectors, overcrowding, medical care, and so on, are frequently encountered in many non-Westernized societies.

This study will investigate the biological perturbations thought to be involved in the Arctic Hysterias of the Innuit Eskimo. They include central nervous system aberrations resulting from chronic middle-ear disease, birth trauma, epilepsy, dietary deficiencies of calcium and vitamin D, and alterations of circadian and circannual biological rhythms. We are not attempting here to discover the organic etiology of the Arctic Hysterias. Instead, we seek to present the individual with Arctic Hysteria in the fullest possible context of his existence which includes interacting cultural, psychological, and biological systems.

BIOLOGY AND PSYCHOLOGY

It is clear, for example, that neurosyphilis severely alters brain physiology. At the same time, the clinical picture of the infected individual is to a major degree affected by cultural and psychodynamic factors. They determine his behavioral response to his CNS lesions. All that he and others around him have learned consciously and unconsciously will color his adaptation to those brain perturbations. Some arrested cases result in manifestly disabling mental disorder; other cases result in minimal impairments to normal overall functioning. Patterns of cultural expectation to changes in behavior may also determine the degree of impairment perceived by the individual. He might be considered permanently tainted, stigmatized, possessed, immoral, or insane. This unfortunate perception may then lead to cognitive damage (Wallace 1961). The individual begins to perceive himself as hopelessly maladjusted. He conforms to this identity by withdrawal, depression, or suicide. On the other hand, certain societies reward unconventional behavior, considering the individual a divine or prophet; or they ignore the behavior altogether if possible.

II. Procedure

THE PREVIOUS CHAPTER outlined the basic synthetic approach to be used in this study to investigate the Arctic Hysterias. According to this approach, the behaviors manifested in these mental disorders represent the outcome of multiple interacting biological, psychological, and historical-cultural systems. The major tasks involved in such a synthetic investigation include: (1) identifying the critical variables associated with the occurrence of the Arctic Hysterias; (2) exploring these variables independently in considerable detail; (3) integrating these complexities in the form of a unified dynamic model. The purpose of this chapter is to consider methods and procedures appropriate to the solution of these major tasks.

IDENTIFYING THE CRITICAL VARIABLES

Defining the critical variables associated with the occurrence of the Arctic Hysterias is the most difficult, and at the same time the most crucial task presented in this investigation. There are a multitude of various kinds of mental disorders, each with its own constellation of etiological theories as any basic text on psychiatry will testify (Noyes and Kolb 1968; Freedman and Kaplan 1967). It is beyond the purposes and scope of this volume to include a general discussion of mental disorders. Likewise, a full presentation of the various etiological approaches to these disorders would be too lengthy and peripheral for inclusion here. These issues will be discussed only as they relate to the particular behavior and problems manifested by the Arctic Hysterias.

Thus the initial problem presented here is one of differential diagnosis, or narrowing down the diagnostic possibilities. This will be accomplished by a detailed examination of the descriptive aspects of the behaviors associated with the Arctic Hysterias. Many of the symptoms will be similar to symptoms characteristic of a number of common psychiatric conditions. The factors known to have etiological significance in each of these disorders will then be examined as they relate to the particular circumstances of the Arctic Hysterias. For example, the convulsive climax of the Arctic Hysteria attack is similar in form to convulsions associated with low serum calcium, magnesium, or glucose; with epilepsy; and with "grand hysteria." Factors associated with each of these conditions will be investigated separately in detail. In addition to a detailed account of the symptoms, we will elicit information regarding the unique situational aspects surrounding the occurrence of the episode. If these events are correlated consistently with the Arctic Hysterias, new etiological directions will be suggested. Wallace (1960) suggested this same procedure be followed in field investigations of Arctic Hysteria among the Eskimos of northern Greenland. He proposed that the general research program be interdisciplinary in scope, and approach the subject according to the following plan:

(1) Collation of data on the reported symptoms, and associated circumstances or attacks ("associated circumstances" including such things as occasions on which attacks occurred, personal history and characteristics of affected persons, cultural and ecological settings syndrome, etc.).
(2) Comparison of the specific symptomatological and circumstantial information with known clinical syndromes.
(3) Selection of the several alternative diagnoses compatible with the symptomatological and circumstantial information, or the formulation of a descriptive diagnosis or diagnoses if no established clinical entity appears to be adequate and the ranking of these diagnoses in terms of their relative probability [Wallace 1960:8-9].

The sources utilized in the preparation of this volume were: (1) review of historical literature and historical documents regarding the occurrence of the Arctic Hysterias in times past; (2) review of current documents regarding the occurrence of the Arctic Hysterias and other mental disorders of circumpolar peoples; (3) statistical analysis of mental health records of Alaskan natives for the year 1968; (4) follow-up from case records and from field experience of individuals reported to manifest behaviors compatible with the Arctic Hysterias; (5) participant observation over the year 1969-70 in an Eskimo village where these behaviors were occasionally manifested.

EXPLORING THE CRITICAL VARIABLES INDEPENDENTLY

After individuals manifesting Arctic Hysteria-like symptoms were identified, and the circumstances of their attacks documented, a list of etiological possibilities was drawn from the vast range of existing psychiatric conditions. The major task presented in this section is one of investigating each of these possibilities in detail, using scientifically developed instruments to either confirm or refute each in the list of possible diagnoses. Wallace had proposed that:

> Once a list of ranked alternative clinical diagnoses has been established, the next steps will be:
> (4) Differential diagnosis confirmed by more intensive observation and interviewing.
> (5) Pursuit of the etiological processes implicated by the confirmed diagnosis.
> Supporting the central stream of investigation must be a continuous process of recording cultural, social, personal, and ecological information from documentary sources and in the field, and the collation of this material with data already obtained, the "jig-saw puzzle" method.
> In the course of this survey, as much information as possible will be obtained on the genealogy and personal history of individuals in order to develop the historical dimension and thus, to provide data both for the evaluation of genetic hypothesis and for the further specification of the symptomatology and surrounding circumstances of the attacks. Neuropsychiatric interviewing and serological tests, and possible other factors, will then lead toward the differential diagnosis, and concurrently with the clinical studies, ethnographic and ecological inquiry will be directed toward a detailed description of community history, the annual cycle of subsistence economy and the dietary, the native conception of disease, and other phenomena necessary to a maximum appreciation of the total culture and ecological matrix. Obviously enough, complete coverage of all of these factors would be impossible even in many seasons of fieldwork; but on the other hand, it is essential to maintain a wide perspective which can turn attention, whenever one central stream of investigation seems to demand it, to studies of ecological relations anywhere from plankton to man and to studies of socio-cultural relations anywhere from personal life histories to community organization [Wallace 1960:8-9].

This study will investigate the following variables which were proposed to be associated with the occurrence of Arctic Hysteria-like behaviors: (1) life history of afflicted individuals; (2) detailed account of symptoms; (3) psychiatric, physical, and neurological examinations; (4) biochemical studies including serum calcium, magnesium, sodium, potassium, chloride, phosphate, glucose, and serology; (5) alterations of biological rhythms including calcium, urinary electrolytes, pulse and blood pressure, fine motor coordination, time estimation, and strength of forearms; (6) skull x-rays; (7) electroencephalography.

The actual rationale and procedures used in investigating each of these variables is, of course, highly complex and beyond the scope of this chapter's discussion. They will, however, be fully detailed in later sections. This in-depth diagnostic procedure was restricted to the population of one small Eskimo village although we were able to include a number of afflicted individuals from nearby villages.

The village was chosen for this field study for several reasons. The first was that our research and statistical analysis of Alaskan native health records indicated that Arctic Hysteria-like behavior was manifest there with greater frequency (six per 350 population) than other villages. Another involved the fact that this village had been recently well studied by anthropologists, and human biologists. Thus, considerable information about the biological and cultural circumstances of this group had been accumulated and was easily accessible. In addition, the village was small enough (< 350) to be dealt with practically, but large enough to present a number of mentally disordered individuals. This society was also fairly isolated, which simplified the problems of defining genetic, ecological and social boundaries.

At this point, attention should be focused on the extremely delicate nature of this fieldwork. Research involving observing, counting, measuring, obtaining biological samples, etc., requires only the cooperation of the subjects under investigation, many of whom might even be paid for their efforts. However, obtaining psychological information which has any meaningful depth requires that a rather special relationship exist between the individual and the researcher. One of the prerequisites to such a relationship is that the subject benefit personally from his experiences with the researcher. This was an explicit operating principle in this fieldwork. A mutually helpful relationship greatly enhances cooperation and probably minimizes distortion of information from the subjects. Furthermore, investigating mental disorder presents an additional, extremely sensitive problem in interrelating between subject and researcher. No individual, regardless of his society, consciously likes to be singled out and studied because of aberrations of mental functioning. No matter how subtle, well-intentioned, and helpful the investigator may be, such an approach assaults the self-integrity of the individual. It is unlikely in such a situation that the subject will reveal much about his inner life; nor will the researcher be able to correspondingly benefit him with treatment. In our own society, individuals suffering from medical and emotional problems frequently avoid seeking help because of the implied assault on their personal integrity. On the other hand, it is well known that many people do seek help for themselves if socially acceptable channels are open to them. Such channels in Eskimo society in the past led to the Shaman, and more recently to the missionary, to the village health aid and occasionally to the school teachers and US Public Health Service nurses and doctors. With this in mind, it was decided that the best introduction to the people of this village would be to identify myself as a general medical doctor with special experience in "conditions of nervous trouble." This role naturally demanded much more than the direct gathering of data related to mental disorders. Colds and respiratory infections were treated, lacerations were sutured, prenatal care administered, the whole gamut of general medical care was given in cooperation with the US Public Health authorities from the nearby field hospital.

Furthermore, establishing an open clinic in the village allowed the people themselves to decide who needed treatment. The individuals with mental disorder discussed in this study initially came to the clinic of their own accord, or were brought by a friend or relative. In no case did the researcher make the initial overtures. Fortunately this proved to be unnecessary, since every person manifesting Arctic Hysteria-like symptoms eventually appeared at the clinic for treatment. We are well aware of the current legal and philosophical issues involving the defining of mental disorder in an individual not wishing to be so defined (Szasz 1970), and are relieved that this did not become a problem in our work.

Another issue involved in this work is that of "professional confidentiality." A physician and anthropologist has certain moral obligations to his patients. Personal confidences may not be publicly identified with the patient. The nature of this study, of course, demands the exposure of considerable amounts of personal material. For this reason the village and villagers involved in this study will remain anonymous.

INTEGRATING THE VARIABLES

The traditional approach to psychiatric problems has been through the medical model which utilizes the process of differential diagnosis in an attempt to distill a single causal variable. This causal element is consequently treated with physical methods, chemicals, psychotherapy, or family—group therapy techniques. The systems approach to be used in this study will attempt to extend rather than reduce the causal chain of events leading to mental disorder. In demonstrating the interaction of multiple variables on biological, psychological, ecological, demographic, and socio-cultural levels, we hope to provide a broader perspective in considering mental disorders. This approach may prove valuable in present day medical and socio-psychiatric care delivery and planning.

Many of the variables proposed here have been studied independently in one form or another in other studies. However, rarely have they been studied in an integrative and synthetic fashion. This investigation is unique in determining the interrelations and interactions among variables such as population size, housing, infectious disease, nutrition, social behaviors, brain pathology, and northern environments as they relate to the Arctic Hysterias. Hopefully this study will provide the general framework for future investigations of disorders other than the Arctic Hysterias in communities other than in the Arctic.

III. The Arctic Hysterias and Related Mental Disorders

MENTAL DISORDERS among the various ethnic and racial groups across the Arctic have been a recurrent subject of intense interest to explorers and anthropologists for over a century. The seemingly high incidence and dramatic nature of such disorders have given rise to many speculations and theorizing as to what causal factors common to all Arctic peoples might be involved. Whether "Arctic Hysteria" represents a disease entity with a common etiology, or a variety of conditions is not at present resolved. In practice, "Arctic Hysteria" encompasses two general types of behavior: the imitative mania which is confined to Siberia; and the frenzied dissociative state which occurs in Siberia, Alaska, Canada, Greenland, and Lappland. Characteristic of both types is a sudden onset usually brought on by fright, a short-lived period of bizarre behavior, and return to normality with the cessation of acute symptoms.

Some authors have felt that the frenzied, dissociative type of "Arctic Hysteria" is so universal in aboriginal peoples of the Arctic as to be characteristic of their race (Czaplicka 1914; Novakovsky 1924). They point out that the imitative type of "Arctic Hysteria" seems to be more prevalent in tribes who have recently migrated to Arctic regions such as Lamuts, Yukaghir, Tungus, and Yakut, and rare in the more ancient inhabitants of this area such as the Chuckchee, Koryak, and Eskimo (Novakovsky 1924). Others have postulated that these acute hysterical outbursts may occur in any isolated group of people living spacially close to one another. They feel that the disorder is probably not related to racial or cultural factors and may be found in such diverse societies as in Mongolia, Malaya, North Africa, Siam, Bengasi, and the Philippines (Aberle 1952). Such cross-cultural comparisons may be useful in stimulating investigators to look for elements which these various societies may have in common. On the other hand, fitting all dissociative types of behavior into a single category called "Latah," or "hysterical-psychosis," with no regard to possible unique cultural, environmental, physiological, or psychological etiologies, may in many cases bypass the crucial issues. Typologies of mental disorder, whether they are based on the official nosological categories of the American Psychiatric Association, or on lay classifications such as "amok" or "Arctic Hysteria," often establish in the investigator a false sense of closure. These "diagnoses" are in fact only syndromes of manifest behavior. The factors associated with any form of manifest behavior are in most cases multiple and varied, and require unique and particular scrutiny. A review of the literature concerning descriptions of "Arctic Hysteria" will provide at least a detail of the characteristic symptoms.

SIBERIA

Imitative types of the "Arctic Hysteria" are called *imu* by the Ainu (Winiarz and Wielawski 1936), *omürax* by the Yukaghir (Jochelson 1926), and *amuyakh* by the Tungus (Czaplicka 1914). These disorders characteristically occur in females more than males, especially during the late teens (Aberle 1952), and at the climacteric (Novakovsky 1924). Symptoms include shouting obscenities, echopraxia, echolalia, suggestibility, wild dancing, and jumping into water or fire (Jochelson 1908). The behavior, in general, is stereotyped and repetitive, the performer being in a hypnotic-like state. Among the Ainu a woman would perform automatic acts of cursing her husband or some other man. This was one of the only occasions which she could do so without retribution. In many of these cases, the precipitating event was a sudden startle. In the case of the

10

Ainu, the startling object was both specific and perhaps symbolic of the underlying conflict. Ainu women greatly fear snakes, which are regarded as having supernatural powers. An encounter with a snake in a dream or in actuality would precipitate the automatic behavior (Winiarz and Wielawski 1936). After the episode, the individual apparently returns to normal, although in many cases there remains some social stigma. At times, individuals are even ostracized after experiencing such an attack (Czaplicka 1914). The episode is usually regarded as spirit possession (Winiarz and Wielawski 1936). An interesting theory accounting for this type of behavior was put forth by Shirokogoff (1935), who felt that *amurakh* represented an individual who unconsciously was responding to cues from his social group. Conflicts existing between members of the group which could not be verbalized or resolved were seen to generate interpersonal anxieties to the point that one member would become an "actor" who hypnotically went through a stylized routine which resulted in a lessening of the groups' internal tensions.

Frenzied dissociative types of "Arctic Hysteria" are called *olonism* by the Samoyed (Yap 1951, 1952), *iu'metun* by the Chuckchee (Bogoras 1909), *mirachit* by the Tungus (Yap 1951, 1952), and *meryak* or *menerik* by the Yuhaghir (Jochelson 1908, 1926). These disorders are most commonly seen in the young woman and in "nervous" young men aspiring to become shamans. Symptoms include loss of appetite, headache, apathy, and indifference to surroundings, which continues for several days. Then, quite suddenly, the afflicted person becomes wild-eyed, and with an air of exaltation begins to chant or speak "in tongues." Arms and legs are often waved about, finally there appear cramps and contractions of the limbs, and often a seizure (Jochelson 1926). Hall (1918) mentions megalomanic boasts of four Tungus afflicted with this form of "Arctic Hysteria." They thought they were gods, and in fact killed one member who had glorified himself too excessively. Bogoras (1909) described a kind of violent nervous affliction which commonly occurred at night among the Chuckchee. During these attacks the individual suffered shortness of breath and often choking sensations. Novakovsky (1924) indicated that the individual often expressed sexual behavior during the attack. Women in the fit of hysteria are said to feel cramps in the vagina and often utter erotic words. He felt that the high incidence of such disorders in the early spring was attributable to rising sexual impulses at that time. Aberle (1952) cites cases of women who reported that the onset of their attacks were precipitated by sexual dreams of being attacked by men or male genitalia. The applications of Freudian theory of these observations are obvious.

Yap (1952:531), on the other hand, feels that the "Arctic Hysterias" are not hysterias at all, but shock or fright neurosis which he feels is more of a psychosomatic mode of response to sudden stress rather than an expression of psychodynamic conflict with its concomitant primary and secondary gain.

The only medically oriented study of these disorders was reported by Grygier (1948) who investigated 150 Zyrians with psychiatric symptoms in the Komi, USSR. He significantly pointed out that virtually fifty percent of his patients were epileptic, forty individuals manifesting hystero-epileptic behavior, by which he probably meant their substratum of epileptic central nervous system pathology was overlaid with many functional components which precipitated and determined the nature of the attacks. The remainder of patients with echolalia, echopraxia, stereotypy, and flexibilitas cerea he felt were classic catatonic schizophrenics.

THE NEW WORLD

The Athabascan Indians at Nulato, Alaska, were reported to occasionally experience episodes of severe hysteria. One such episode was reported by Dall (1870:171-172) who observed,

> The patient fell in a sort of convulsion, struggled violently, appearing unconscious, tearing the clothing and breaking everything within reach. There were no symptoms of any disease and the fits were epidemic, seizing one after another at short intervals. The cases resembled the descriptions of those who in ancient times were supposed to be bewitched, and also some of those appearances which have accompanied cases of semireligious mania in Europe in modern times. Suspecting the cause of the symptoms, I recommended the applications of a birch twig, well laid on: the result exceeded my anticipation. The patients arose in a rage and the epidemic

was effectively checked . . . It is probably that in the course of time these fits, at first willful, become in a measure involuntary.

Among the Nelson Indians there also were many episodes of hysterical behavior. Honigmann (1949) reported that around 1930 a group of these Indians fled from their camp and sat in the snow. He felt this may have represented an outbreak of true Arctic Hysteria with compulsive suggestibility.

The frenzied, dissociative types of "Arctic Hysteria" have appeared in literature on the Eskimo with great frequency, where they have been termed *pibloktoq*. It was the impression of many early authorities that the most striking aspect of the state of the aboriginal Eskimo was the relative absence of physical diseases and the prevalence of mental disease. Actually, it appears that both physical and mental disorders were common enough. As early as 1820, Cranz (1820:214-216) observed that fainting, apoplexy, epilepsy, lunacy, and madness commonly affected the Eskimo of Greenland. Somewhat later, Rink (1875:56-57) reported,

> Pindlingayak means a fool, and Pindlerortok a mad or delerious person. By degrees, as madness increases, disturbing the operation of the senses and clouding the judgment and insight into things present, the absent or concealed things and the events of the future unfold themselves to the inner sight of the sane. A Pindlerortok was even gifted with a faculty of walking upon the water, besides the highest perfection in divining, but was at the same time greatly feared; whereas the Pindlingayak, being also clairvoyant, was esteemed a useful companion to the inhabitants of a hamlet.

By the turn of the century, expeditions to the north, especially through Greenland, became more frequent, and so did reports of *pibloktoq*. In 1911, Whitney wrote:

> September—It was upon our return to Etah on the evening of the sixteenth that I observed for the first time a case of piblokto among the natives. Piblokto is a form of temporary insanity to which the Highland Eskimo are subject, and which comes upon them very suddenly and unexpectedly. They are liable to have these attacks more particularly at the beginning or during the period of darkness. Tukshu began suddenly to rave upon leaving the boat. He tore off every stitch of clothing he had on and would have thrown himself into the water of the Sound, but for the restraint of the Eskimos. He seemed possessed of supernatural strength, and it was all that four men could do to hold him. With the knowledge that his madness was temporary and he would shortly be himself again, with no serious consequences to follow, I cheerfully watched his astonishing contortions. It would have been a very serious matter, however, had Tukshu been attacked while in the boat; and it is very serious indeed when piblokto attacks one, as it sometimes does, when on the trail, or at a time when there are insufficient men to care for the afflicted one [Whitney 1911:67].

> Around October 9—beginning of winter, polar night coming, winds die down, quiet, feeling of impending gloom. Women felt depressed, but mainly worried about safety of hunters who had gone into interior to hunt caribou. Wives of Kulutinguak and Kudlar cry and moan for husbands. They (the women) were very short of food and killed three of their dogs to eat . . . At half-past one that night I was awakened from a sound sleep by a woman shouting at the top of her voice—shrill and startling, like one gone mad. I knew at once what it meant—someone had gone piblokto. I tumbled into my clothes and rushed out. Far away on the driving ice of the Sound, a lone figure was running and raving. The boatswain and Billy joined me; and, as fast as we could struggle through three feet of snow, with drifts often to the waist, we gave pursuit. At length I reached her, and to my astonishment she struggled desperately, and it required the combined strength of the three of us to get her back to the shack where she was found to be in bad shape—one hand was frozen slightly and part of one breast. After a half hour of quiet she became rational again, but the attack left her very weak [Whitney 1911:82-83].

> On the evening after the hunters returned, (the next evening and while I was dressing Kudlar's hip) Tungive—Kulutinguah Kooner—was again attacked by piblokto. She rushed out of the igloo, tore her clothing off and threw herself into a snow drift. I ran to Kulutinguah's assistance, but the woman was strong as a lion, and we had all we could do to hold her. A strong north wind was blowing, with a temperature eight degrees below zero, and I thought she would surely be severely frozen before we could get her into the igloo again; but, in some miraculous manner, she escaped even the slightest frostbite. After getting her in the igloo, she grew weak as a kitten, and it was several hours before she became quite herself. In connection with this woman's case, it is curious and interesting to note that, previous to the attack which she had suffered the day before the return of the hunting party, she had never shown any symptoms of piblokto [Whitney 1911:87].

. . . Men had been suddenly adrift on pan ice and had found a loose ice pan connection to the shore ice. All save Tukshu had crossed . . . feared he would have to be abandoned . . . Tukshu then appeared with his dog team . . . All aided Tukshu fell into water when ice pan broke. He was hauled onto the shore ice and immediately took off his wet clothes. He was given whiskey and began to exercise. I do not know whether it was the whiskey or the excitement attendant upon his narrow escape, but suddenly Tukshu went piblokto, and nearly two hours elapsed before he was sufficiently recovered for us to begin our retreat [Whitney 1911:181].

January—While we were thus engaged, the Eskimos laughing as they talked and ate and enjoying themselves to the utmost, Tukshu, without warning or hint, went piblokto. He fought the others like a demon, and I thought he would surely break through the side of the igloo; but finally, though the Eskimos did their utmost to keep him in, he passed out through the entrance. In the tussle nearly all his clothing was torn off; and in the bitter and intense cold it seemed to me that he must certainly freeze. For an hour he wandered around in the snow, while the others watched him through holes they had cut in the igloo's side. Then he was captured and taken into one of the stone habitations [Whitney 1911:187].

About the same time Steensby (1910) who had studied the Polar Eskimo of Greenland, reported:

In July I was witness of such an attack in the woman, Inadtliak. It lasted 25 minutes. She sat on the ground with the legs stretched out, swaying her body to and fro sometimes rapidly, sometimes more slowly, from side to side and tortuously, whilst she kept her hands comparatively still and only now and then moved her elbows in to her sides. She stared out in front of her, quite regardless of her surroundings, and sang or screamed, occasionally changing the tone, iah-iah-iaha-ha . . .; now and then she interjected a sentence, e.g., that now the Danish had at last come to them, and again the great happiness this gave her now in the glad summer time, and so on. Her two small children sat and played about her, whilst the members of the tribe scarcely looked at her during the attack; they seemed to be very well acquainted with such things. She recovered quite suddenly and only some red spots on her cheeks indicated anything unusual. Without so much as looking about her or betraying a sign of anything unusual, she began literally, in the same moment to give her youngest child milk and then to quietly chew a skin [Steensby 1910:377].

Robert Peary resided in this area at that time too, while attempting to attain the North Pole. He observed:

There exists among these people a form of hysteria known as piblokto (the same name as given to the well-known madness among their dogs), with which women, more frequently than men, are affected. During these spells, the maniac removes all clothing and prances about like a broncho. In 1898, while the Windward was in winter quarters off Cape D'Urville, a married woman was taken with one of these fits in the middle of the night. In a state of perfect nudity she walked the deck of the ship; then, seeking still greater freedom, jumped the rail, onto the frozen snow and ice. It was some time before we missed her; and, when she was finally discovered, it was at a distance of half a mile, where she was still pawing and shouting to the best of her abilities. She commenced a wonderful performance of mimicry in which every conceivable cry of local bird and mammal was reproduced in the throat of Inaloo. This same woman at other times attempts to walk the ceiling of her igloo; needless to say, she has never succeeded.

A case of piblokto lasts from five minutes to half-an-hour or more. When it occurs under cover of a hut, no apparent concern is felt by other inmates, nor is any attention paid to the antics of the mad one. It is only when an attempt is made to run abroad that the cords of restraint are felt [Peary 1907:384-385].

Aside from rheumatism and bronchial troubles, the Eskimos are fairly healthy; but the adults are subject to a peculiar affliction which they call piblokto, a form of hysteria. I have never known a child to have piblokto, but someone among the adult Eskimos would have an attack every day or two, and one day there were five cases. The immediate cause of this affection is hard to trace, though sometimes it seems to be the result of a brooding over absent or dead relatives, or a fear of the future. The manifestations of this disorder are somewhat startling.

The patient, usually a woman, begins to scream and tear off and destroy her clothing. If on the ship, she will walk up and down the deck, screaming and gesticulating, and generally in a state of nudity, though the thermometer may be in the minus forties. As the intensity of the attack increases, she will sometimes leap over the rail upon the ice, running perhaps half a mile. The attack may last a few minutes, an hour, or even more; and some sufferers become so wild that they would continue running about on the ice perfectly naked until they froze to death, if they were not forcibly brought back.

When an Eskimo is attacked with piblokto indoors nobody pays much attention, unless the sufferer should reach for a knife or attempt to injure someone. The attack usually ends in a fit of weeping; and when the patient quiets down, the eyes are bloodshot, the pulse high and the whole body trembles for an hour or so afterwards. [Peary 1910:166-167].

During the same expedition, Peary's wife recorded in her journal:

The mistress of the remaining igloo was making an awful noise and trying to come out of her habitation, while a man was holding her back and talking to her, but she screamed and struggled so long as we remained where she could see us. I asked Mane what was the nature of the trouble, and she told me that the woman was piblokto (mad) [Peary 1893:125].

Peary's lieutenant, MacMillan, was also struck with the dramatic nature of *pibloktoq* and colorfully wrote:

Pibloktoq was now common among the women. What this disease is no one knows. I believe, however, that it is a form of hysteria, not caused by fright or joy or sorrow, but possibly by jealousy, abuse by the husband, or a craving for affection. After crooning for a time, accompanied by a swaying back and forth of the body and a beating of the hands, with an "I don't care" yell, they were off for the hills or Polar Sea, ripping off their clothes with teeth and hands, spitting, biting, clawing, if restrained in any way. Heavens, what a time! The show was always well attended. Everybody was up to see what would happen next and something always did happen with startling rapidity. We found fat, old In-a-loo flat on her back far out on the packed drift ice, blowing like a porpoise and cramming pieces of ice under her sealskin coat on her bare breast. We handled her with gloves. Although she was well along in years, she could certainly scratch and kick. With a sling around her waist, the boys "heave ho'ed" her over the rail. Her husband promptly sat down on her feet, a son on each arm, and a ladyfriend on her head, and there they remained until the tumult subsided. Weak, dazed and with eyes blood-shot, she was finally put to bed. When in the unlady-like condition of "piblokto" her special forte was an insane desire, followed by the attempt to walk across the ceilings of our cabins. Commander Peary informed me that when "possessed by the Devil," as the Eskimos think they are, this particular woman was adept at imitating the noises of birds and the cries of all the animals of the north. Ahl-nay-ah, nicknamed Buster by the men, was the star actress. Her performance was "impeccable," as the dramatic critics say. She was the most accomplished singer on board. Without the singing, a woman about to have piblokto really could not do her best, for the curtain rings up with music to attract attention. Our chief engineer, dear old George Wardwell, dead now, weighed two hundred and forty pounds and wore union suits. Buster weighed a scant one hundred and had no union suits. The chief would have given away his heart. Buster was now well clothed; by wrapping the garment around her twice, she had two union suits! it was a well-established and accepted fact that women like good clothes and want us to know they have good clothes. In silence of one mid-afternoon out popped Buster from Eskimo headquarters and, with a Commanche yell, cleared the rail. She had it on! The pleats were out. She looked like an animated misshaped ballon. Pursued by a highly interested conclave of sailors, she struggled valiantly to gain the first rampart beyond the box house. She fought hard, but she was finally captured and subdued and led back to the ship, hair streaming, lips protruding, and blowing like a bandmaster every note in the scale and some beyond it. No one knew exactly what to do with her, since she had no husband, the only woman in the tribe who hadn't, and consequently there was no one to take charge of the runaway. Someone suggested, "Lash her up!" She was wrapped in a blanket, arms pinned to her sides, flat on her back on a two-inch plank, and hoisted up to the fore boom where she remained, swinging to and fro in the wind, not all faculties subdued, for she could still sing and spit, which she did high into the air! Life was not monotonous on the Roosevelt at the edge of the Polar Sea [MacMillan 1934:101-102].

In the Angamagsalik area of Greenland, Holm (1914) observed that often when a person had a high fever with a headache, the Angakok (shaman) was summoned. The Angakok stated that the person must confess that he was a witch, or he would become raving mad. If madness ensued, the afflicted individual was bound with hands and feet, stretched out on the platform on the floor, and gagged. He was not given food or drink, and sometimes heavy stones were laid on his chest. It was felt that the only way to relieve the madness was to induce the person to confess.

The famed Arctic explorer, Knud Rasmussen, also observed cases of Arctic Hysteria at this time and related several hair-raising accounts. In one case, Qitdlugtoq, a young man, became quite wild. He shouted, attempted to walk onto the sea, and tried to harpoon onlookers. He did not seem to see anyone, however, but maintained a fixed stare ahead. He sang songs of the dead and suddenly tried to run up the side of a cliff. He ran into a man's tent and pulled a knife which was quickly taken from him. The attack subsided and he regained consciousness (Rasmussen 1915).

Knud Rasmussen's son, Neils, lived in Greenland from 1939 to 1945, during which time he too witnessed episodes of *pibloktoq*. Some of his accounts are as follows:

May 1941—Patiluk
On hunting trip north of Annatoak (about 10 miles). With two Eskimos, 17-18 years of age. One Eskimo lean and thin, quite sophisticated and quick to learn. Other Eskimo, Patiluk was heavy set and "simple minded." Had been successful in hunting as they had secured for men and dogs. Everyone was healthy and in good spirits. The Eskimos decided to return to the settlement by way of the ice cap instead of following the sea ice around Cape Alexander. The sun was very bright at this time. The men were very sunburned and darkly tanned. On leaving the sea ice they found that the snow had melted completely from the ground. They were faced with the prospect of dragging their sleds over the muddy and stony ground, or leaving them there and returning on foot. The latter possibility closed, as this would mean ridicule for the hunters.

They plodded over the bare ground. It took them five days of hard labor to bring the sleds up to the glacier. During this time, the men had eider ducks to eat, but they had no dog rations. Neils Rasmussen said he had worn out four pairs of boots during the trip over the bare ground. The land was without game, hot and muddy. They reached the glacier and succeeded in making their way up to the crest. Their way was now easy. It was a downhill slope to the settlement. All breathed a sigh of relief. Patiluk suddenly began to beat his dogs with the handle of his whip, while screaming incoherently and dancing about. He struck the dogs so hard that he broke the whip handle. Patiluk then began to cut the dogs loose from their leads. The total time of the attack was five minutes. He stopped his action with the dogs and the attack was over. Patiluk at this time retained control of bladder and bowels. Patiluk did not remember events, as when he took up his whip, he was surprised to find it broken.

Nekri-Ataqahengwak
Neils Rasmussen stayed with couple of Eskimos in skin tent (summer). He heard woman cry out in nearby tent. She howled like a dog, but very loud. Rasmussen said he didn't know how she could make such a loud noise. The woman howled intermittently for 20 minutes. He inquired what it was and Eskimos said, "Oh, that's only Ataqahengwak," and dismissed the event. Rasmussen did not see her, but assumed that husband able to restrain her. Did not regard it as pibloktok at the time. Feels now that could have been such a case.

Neils Rasmussen told that two men did not take part in drum dance as they would become too excited and then would run berserk. These men were said to be violent and dangerous to others. Some men are dangerous, that is, they can be potentially dangerous to other people, as they do intend while pibloktoq to harm people. Rasmussen felt the reason they generally do not is that someone is following the person having the attack to prevent him from injuring himself or someone else. "They take care of each other."

In one case Neils Rasmussen was a passenger on a sled driven by a very simple, friendly, not too bright young man, always friendly, untalkative, but reliable fellow. They had had some trouble on the land before they got to the ice cap, very tough going, no snow and very tough work. Finally they reached the ice cap which meant safety and then they had some smooth going, of course, and they would be home in a day or two. N.R. thought that everything was alright with him. Had his back towards him; he was standing in front of the sled and disentangling the dogs. He heard him talk very strangely, didn't understand a word of it. Suddenly he began to kick the dogs, one or two of them. Then systematically he started to kick them all, talking louder and louder until he was screaming unintelligibly. He warmed up for a minute or so that way; and after about a minute or so he was in full swing, screaming all the time. He tore all the stuff off the sleds, skins, boxes, stoves, and hurled them at the dogs. It lasted about 10 minutes . . .It didn't do much harm to the dogs, in fact nothing at all, couldn't hit them actually.

All of a sudden it was over. He sat down on the sled exhausted. A short attack. Later, days later when they got back to the village, he had a lot of fun about it. The other companions on the trip kidded the fellow about his behavior, and the young boy himself always asked Neils Rasmussen whether he had been scared; it is not a disgrace that these things happen. It can happen to anybody. It's a natural incident. It usually turns into a funny story . . . [Steed 1947-48:205-206].

N.R. has seen another "bird" (man) rolling in the snow without any clothes on, completely naked, for about a half hour. That is what usually happens. Knud Rasmussen described it that way too; they tear off their clothes. N.R. saw only one instance of this, but it's supposed to be a common characteristic [Steed 1947-48:207].

One was a girl who suddenly decided she wanted a piece of seaweed, and without a stitch on waded into the sea, still open water, and it was bitter cold, way below freezing point. She waded out dangerously—she had hardly a foothold, she was out so far, got the seaweed, came back triumphantly and with great dignity, and with the same dignity she suddenly threw it away again. All of a sudden her dignity broke completely, she started screaming and made a continual somersault. She could not have done that in a sober state, must have been a couple of hundred feet. She was so exhausted that she slept for 15 hours or so [Steed 1947-48: 207-208].

Knud Rasmussen tells an incident reported by N.R. of a man who "had more than one" (inebriated). He suddenly climbed up a steep cliff, bluff outside the village, completely vertical. Climbed up to the top of those, although obviously humanly impossible to do it, but he did somehow. There is no doubt that he could not have possibly done it under normal circumstances. Then he grabbed the knife and went into a tent where three little children were sleeping; they were alone there, but the father of the children followed the man, quietly took the knife out of the hand, and that moment the man collapsed [Steed 1947-48:208].

General statements by Neils Rasmussen:
Certain things are common to all people...they are always completely oblivious to their surroundings; they are always strongly agitated, have a feverish light in their eyes, talk very fast but completely unintelligibly; and their speech makes no sense, "speaking in tongues," so to say, just jabbering away, but not in the Eskimo language. There is no way of telling where and when it may come. Some people feel it coming. In...severe cases, they become completely exhausted and go to sleep for 12 hours, completely drained of all strength, do most fantastic things, completely idiotic, picking up all kinds of junk outside the house, carrying it into the house as if they found some great treasure. Or the person in question may decide that he wants a little stone he sees way up on top of the mountain. He will go and get it, naked sometimes. Women don't behave differently from men. Eskimos believe it is an absolutely natural phenomenon. They don't fear it [Steed 1947-48:204-205, 207, 209].

In his novel, The Last Kings of Thule, Malaurie recorded:

One evening when the father and one of his sons went to eat seal with some neighbors, the mother remained lying down, saying that she was tired. The father and son talked, ate and drank tea with the neighbors. They were both very excited, for one Eskimo said that he had seen fresh traces of a bear not far from the encampment. Suddenly, towards midnight, they heard the dogs howl.

"Let's go back," said the father. "Something is wrong over there. I feel it here," and he pointed to his skull.

Outside, the dogs were barking for all they were worth. Meanwhile the wind had risen. The son went first. They could see the igloo light, which seemed to shine and then go out. One would have said that somebody was passing backwards and forwards ceaselessly before the only window. In front of the house the dogs were dragging with all their strength at their leads. When the father and son opened the door they saw a horrible sight. The house was upside-down. Torn caribou skins were strewn on the floor in the midst of seal-meat and streams of blood. The mother, her face black and congested was running backwards and forwards, with her clothes in disorder and an oulou (round knife used by women) in her hand.

The children were trembling in a corner. The sound of the door made her jump. Suddenly she leapt, but the father was on her before she had taken three steps. Disturbed by her cries, men hurried from all sides. The unhappy woman broke free and ran off, with hardly any clothes towards the sea-ice in spite of the cold. She still held her knife, and without stopping picked up everything that seemed solid—pebbles, wood and so on. When she felt the men coming too close, she threw everything at them over her shoulder. If she saw dogs' droppings, she smelt at them, rubbed her face with them and then gluttonously devoured the rest. The men pursued her to an iceberg. She tried to haul herself up, but she was badly shod and slid down. But she hung on to a spur, and finally managed to sit astride an ice-ridge. From here, she cursed the men who surrounded her. One last time she managed to get away. Running towards the sea-ice which was broken up by the storm, she leapt from ice-floe to ice-floe and defied her pursuers. Her situation was terrible. Every moment she almost fell into the water. Fortunately, her strength suddenly failed, and the Innuit managed to reach her not far from the camp.

The woman was exhausted by then. They tied her on the sled, and, trembling with fever, she was taken back to the warm igloo. Her face was pale. She had lost consciousness and rapidly fell into a heavy agitated sleep. When she woke some hours later, she remembered nothing.

The cases of piblocta (hysteria) were frequent among women, said the Eskimo. But one no longer saw such serious ones. And these hysterias have never killed anybody as far as I know. In spite of these details his story seemed exaggerated to me. But it was to surprise me far less when later I learned what had happened to Rasmussen.

In 1907, on his first expedition, also at the beginning of the winter, Rasmussen was nearly the victim of an hysterical subject. He was writing at his table when he heard shrill cries outside. Immediately he went to his window of stretched intestines, where, according to custom—and as one can still find at Nekri and Kekertak—a little hole was made in the center so that one could see what went on outside. Just at the moment when he was putting his eye to the hole a knife tore the window. Rasmussen—lightly wounded—curled himself in a corner of the room and wiped his face. Then a rain of stones came in. The Eskimos ran up, but here, as in the previous story, it was impossible to secure the man immediately. On the advice of friends, Rasmussen came out of his dwelling. The possessed man chased him. It was a moonless night. Rasmussen could not run, hindered by his boots, which he had not had time to lace properly. At each step he slid, but the other grew breathless, and the Eskimos managed at last to seize him [Malaurie 1956:78-80].

Danish medical investigators working in this area have likewise been impressed with the apparent prevalence of psychopathology. Bertelsen (1905) felt that these people were in general quite unstable, being prone to impulsiveness and suggestibility. He observed several small "psychotic epidemics" and noted that the people in general seemed uncritical when confronted with a patient who considered himself the instrument of God. A more recent study conducted by Ehrstrom (1951) included a series of 1073 Eskimos whom he examined for medical and emotional disorders. Of these, he found twenty cases of pure hysteria, presumably of the dissociative or conversion types, twenty-six cases of "kayak phobia" (fear of being alone in the kayak at sea) and eighty-one cases of psychophysiological disorders. He concluded that the incidence of hysterical neurosis was higher, and psychophysiological disorders lower, than among peoples in more intense contact with Western civilization. On the basis of this finding, Parker (1962:78) speculates that perhaps in the past the dramatic forms of Arctic Hysteria were more common, and that psychophysiological disorders are now becoming increasingly prevalent as more and more contact is maintained with the Western world.

Hysteria has been observed among the Eskimo in other areas of the Arctic as well. The Eskimos of the Hudson Bay region still distinguish hysterical behavior from other forms of behavioral disturbance, such as epilepsy, acute melancholic withdrawal, and depression with paranoid hostility (Valee 1966). Several cases which Jane Hughes (1960) felt resembled *pibloktoq* were observed among the Eskimos of St. Lawrence Island, Alaska. Her informant related:

Once and awhile X does acting, slapping faces, screwed around . . . I thought at first she was partly shaman out of mind a little bit I think . . . I've heard something . . . hollering behind me, it was X. I seen her a little bit, she was making faces like that with wrinkled eye, she was winking her one eye so tight and seems to me that part of her face was shrinking. I didn't look, I hates to keep looking at her like this, scared me so much. I think she was out of mind . . . But few minutes afterwards, she is become Okay [Hughes 1960:68].

In her survey of the inhabitants of Sivokok, Alaska, she found forty-six individuals neurotic and thirty-five with psychophysiological disorders, which roughly corresponds to the frequencies of these disorders cited by Ehrstrom in Greenland. In addition, there were twenty people with organic brain syndromes, nineteen mentally defectives, and six psychotics. Interestingly, she discovered eighteen who manifested seizures (Hughes 1960).

Regarding Arctic Hysteria in Alaska, Nachman, a psychologist with the US Public Health Service, recently reported,

We do not have at present any accurate record of the incidence of hysterical spells which might be closely related to [Arctic Hysteria], but our clinical experience suggests that they are not infrequent. One typical kind of account is of a teenage girl who has sudden outbursts of excited behavior, sometimes with convulsions or paralysis or anesthesias for which no organic basis can be found, who yells and tears her clothes and performs some bizarre acts, then becomes drowsy, and is later amnesic for the experience. Another is of the man in his 20's or 30's who had spells (again sometimes giving rise to suspicions of convulsive disorders which remain unconfirmed) of sudden violence in which he will tear up the house, shoot up the town, or take off onto the tundra ill-clothed in severe weather.

The documentation of the meaning of such episodes has usually been too fragmentary to permit any definitive statements about them. The fragments, however, suggest that they often serve in the case of the girls, as protests about sexual threats and temptations which cannot safely be acknowledged and in the case of the men, as escapes from humiliations around the inability to meet the responsibilities of married life.

There is still another set of behaviors—child beatings which also show many of these characteristics . . . (they have not been studied in Alaska though their occurrence in both white and "native" populations is reported to be high). The essential dynamic here, as in the other kinds of episodes we have considered—is a sudden loss of control in an otherwise reasonable person—frequently with either denial or genuine amnesia for the act afterward—and in a person who, because of the severe deprivations he has himself suffered and the influx of demands that he cannot meet—reacts with rage and violence at the childishness of the child and its requirement that he himself be a responsible adult [Nachman 1969:7-11].

On the basis of some of these reports, a number of documentary researchers have proposed several interesting theories to account for the Arctic Hysteria syndrome. First among these was the noted psychoanalyst and translator of Freud, A. A. Brill. Brill interviewed Peary's lieutenant, Donald MacMillan, regarding his observations of the Eskimos and *pibloktoq* during the attainment of the North Pole. MacMillan remarked that *pibloktoq* reminded him of a little child discouraged and unhappy because he imagined that no one loved him or cared for him and therefore runs away (Brill 1913:517). Brill built on this theme in generating his hypothesis and concluded that,

this plainly shows that just as in civilized people, it is love that plays the great part in the causation of the malady . . . the greatest determinant of pibloktoq is sex in all its broad ramifications. This, too, corresponds with our psychoanalytic experiences gained among our own women, where contrary to the prevailing opinion of some, the gross sexual [heterosexual intercourse] does not necessarily play the great role in the determination of the hysterical symptoms [Brill 1913:518].

He went on to point out that Eskimos do not manifest conversion-type neurosis, nor do male Eskimos suffer from *pibloktoq*. He felt conversion-type neurosis occurred only in people with "complex psychic organizations," and Eskimos were too unsophisticated for this disorder. However, we have already cited five males who suffered from *pibloktoq*, and the investigations of Ehrstrom (1951) who found many cases of conversion-type hysterias among the Eskimos.

At any rate, Brill concluded that like children, the Eskimo has not as yet acquired the necessary ego mechanisms for repression of impulses, and therefore no definite line of demarcation between conscious and unconscious exists. Their neuroses are correspondingly not as complicated and hidden as those of "grown-up and intelligent adults."

They may evince themselves in crying spells, screaming spells, or some other simple manifestations . . . There is hardly anything more childish than the imitation of the dog or bird, or the running away into the hills singing or crying. And yet, is there really so much difference between the hysterical mechanisms as evidenced in pibloktoq and the grande hysterie or other modern hysterical manifestations? We may answer unhesitatingly that the difference is more apparent than real [Brill 1913:519-520].

In a study equally far removed from the primary subjects, but more rigorously utilizing secondary sources, Gussow (1960) attempted to define *pibloktoq* and formulate its etiology phenomenologically. Based on many of the cases cited previously in this paper, he summarized the symptomatology into the following categories according to the frequency of their occurrence:

1. Tearing off of clothing, achieving partial or complete nudity. This was frequently one of the first behavioral signs of the attack.
2. Glossolalia, mutterings, meaningless syllables, "speaking in tongues," making animal sounds.
3. Fleeing across the tundra, wandering into hills, if outdoors, running back and forth in an agitated state.
4. Rolling into the snow, placing ice on oneself, jumping into water.
5. Bizarre acts such as attempting to walk on ceiling, hoarding odd objects, etc.
6. Throwing things and thrashing about.
7. Mimetic acts [Gussow 1960:226].

Most significant is the fact that during these attacks the individual appears to be in a daze, out of conscious contact with those around him. The episodes last from several minutes to several hours, and are often accompanied or terminated with epileptotetanoid seizures. Carpo-pedal spasms resulting from simultaneous tonic contractions of the flexor and extensor muscles of the forearms and feet are an obvious part of these seizures in photos of a woman going *pibloktoq* which were taken by MacMillan and which are now preserved at the American Museum of Natural History (see Appendix A).

The attack is often preceded by irritability, photophobia, confusion and inactive depression for several hours or days. After the episode, the individual is apparently exhausted and often falls off into sleep. Following this, he is again normal mentally and in contact with his surroundings. Routine activities are resumed. There is reportedly amnesia for the event.

Gussow (1960) felt that *pibloktoq* does not represent the behavior of mentally disordered individuals. Instead, he believed it to be the basic way Eskimos in general reacted to situations of intense stress. Food supplies in the winter often were very low or depleted, and Gussow suggested that the Eskimo unconsciously perceived this season as a most insecure and stressful time; thus, the emphasis on rituals such as "The Messenger Feast" during this time of year. Winter was also the time of the shamans, and not unexpectedly the time of going *pibloktoq*.

Like Brill, Gussow emphasized the Eskimo's psychological ability to regress and act out his "infantile" needs for love and emotional support. The frequently reported running off on the ice or tundra was analyzed as the afflicted individual's desire to be pursued and attended to. In other words, the Eskimo is here seen to respond to stress and feelings of helplessness, by resorting to the same expressions of frustration often utilized by children in our own society, i.e., the temper tantrum.

In a later paper on this subject, Parker (1962) lumped *pibloktoq* with hysterical disorders reported from other societies. He concluded that there were certain practices and beliefs which rendered some societies more hysterogenic than others. He found that hysterical behavior tended to prevail in societies:

a) Where early socialization experiences are not severe and involve minimal repression of dependency needs and sexual drives. In such societies, where there is relatively high gratification of dependency needs, the modal superego structure will not be severe or rigid.
b) Where there is an emphasis on communalistic values, a relatively great amount of face-to-face cooperative patterns, and high expectations of mutual aid.
c) Where the female role involves considerable disadvantages and lower self-esteem compared to the role of the male.
d) Where the religious system involves beliefs in supernatural possession, and where "hysterical-like" behavior models are provided in the institutionalized religious practices [Parker 1962:81].

Most Eskimo societies, he feels, conform to these characteristics. Eskimos in general experience minimal frustration of their dependency and affection needs during early childhood. They learn quickly that they can depend on relatives and others for nurturance and prompt satisfaction of their needs. Thus, they presumably never develop the basic psychological defense mechanisms used to ward off frustrating ungratified wishes from the conscious awareness, i.e., repression and denial. Repression and denial are psychological functions which render wishes and frustrations unconscious. They are the mechanisms through which one can "forget" ungratified needs and wishes. Psychoanalytic theory holds, however, that such needs and wishes are not really forgotten, but remain unrecognized by the individual. The realm of such unrecognized wishes has been termed the unconscious. Unconscious needs and impulses, however, are felt to provide the energy for the individual to pursue substitute gratifications. Such substitute gratifications may take the form of work, art, or elaborations or thoughts resulting in philosophy or folklore, etc. At times, such substitute gratification is psychopathological, resulting in nonproductive ritual or thought rumination. Furthermore, it is felt that repression is a prerequisite to the development of the superego, a psychological structure which unconsciously and automatically provides one with a sense of proper and improper behavior. When an individual's impulses are in conflict with his superego, guilt and anxiety are experienced, which tends to maintain his behavior within socially acceptable bounds. The Eskimo, according to some authorities as cited previously, lacks a well formed superego and correspondingly lacks true guilt as a mechanism of social control. Instead, group opinion and shame are the methods used to maintain socially acceptable behavior. Essentially, Parker's formulation does not differ from Brill's or

Gussow's. All postulate that the Eskimo has not learned to repress his primary wishes and impulses; that his wishes and impulses are, therefore, available anytime for conscious expression; that because of this he has little superego structure and maintains social control externally through ridicule-shame methods. In addition, Parker points out that the shamanistic practices of the Eskimo provide socially-sanctioned outlets for hostility, and in fact, the very role-model for hysterical behavior. Combining this proposition with the notion that *pibloktoq* is a behavior basic to psychology of the shaman himself, suggests a self-reinforcing model of basic personality interacting with a social institution as follows:

PIBLOKTOQ ⇄ SHAMANISM

Recently Wallace (1960) has proposed that the Arctic Hysterias might profitably be investigated from still another direction. In discussing the etiology of this mental disorder, he turned attention to the obvious, but for the most part, long overlooked ecological determinants of psychological functioning. He cited earlier investigators such as Novakovsky (1924), who felt the Arctic Hysterias were precipitated by such environmental factors as the extreme cold and the "long Polar night" during the winter months. A more credible hypothesis was later suggested by two Scandinavian investigators, who studied nutritional deficiencies in Greenland. During a health survey among the Angmaggsalik in 1936-37, Hoygaard (1941:72) found dietary deficiencies in calcium and also noted the extreme proclivity of these people for "hysterical fits." Baashuus-Jessen (1935) reported epileptotetanoid behavior in dogs (also termed pibloktoq by the Eskimos) which he felt was caused by dietary vitamin and mineral deficiencies, principal among these, calcium. Wallace considered that the low calcium diet plus the low vitamin D_3 synthesis during the dark winter months possibly rendered the Eskimo hypocalcemic at this time. Anxiety from chronic stress or sudden fright frequently leads an individual to hyperventilate, which may further lower the levels of ionized serum calcium by raising the pH of the serum. The interaction of these physiological factors was hypothesized to lower serum calcium to levels which could impair the functioning of the central nervous system. In such a state of nervous excitability, normal cognitive functions would become distorted and pibloktoq behaviors would ensue. Seizures, and especially tetany which have been reported as terminating the pibloktoq episodes, are also commonly associated with symptoms of hypocalcemia. With such diagnostic speculations in mind, Wallace then formulated the interdisciplinary approach previously cited in Chapter II. The "calcium hypothesis" was investigated in North Alaskan villages and will be discussed in more detail in another section.

Wallace's main contribution to this subject was not the mere suggestion of a hypocalcemic diagnosis for pibloktoq. It was more far-reaching in nature. It focused for the first time on possible physiological factors involved in mental disorders in non-Western societies, and implied future models of interaction between physiological, psychological, cultural, and environmental systems. He rightly recognized that certain diseases and environmental perturbations can affect the functioning of the central nervous system, and thus psychology and behavior itself.

It should be emphasized that such organic formulations by no means negate psychological and historo-cultural determinants of behavior. In fact, Wallace points to their articulation by stating that such "incipient neurological disfunction is susceptible to different interpretations by the victim and his associates and can therefore precipitate different overt responses, depending on particular customs of the individual and group" (Wallace 1961:270).

RELATED MENTAL DISORDERS OF THE ESKIMO

Perhaps because of its dramatic nature and historical relevance, pibloktoq has received much attention in the literature. There are, however, several other mental disorders unique to the situation of the Eskimo. They merit discussion here since many of the psychological mechanisms responsible for these disorders may also be applicable to the Arctic Hysterias.

Kayak Phobia

> When hunters row out their kayaks in the still water, they are often becalmed with the sun's bright glare reflected in their eyes, as from a mirror. Suddenly, as they wait patiently for seals to rise to the surface, they are gripped with a paralysis which prevents their moving a muscle. They sit as if petrified, and they say they have a feeling that the water is rising over them, but they cannot lift a hand. Then, if a slight wind curls the surface of the sea, they are freed of the spell and come out of it. The poor victims often become so frightened that after one experience they never dare venture out alone again [Freuchen 1935:242].

This experience has occurred rather commonly to Greenland Eskimos and is called Kayak-Angst, Kayak-dread, or Kayak phobia. As many as ten to fifteen percent of all hunters in Greenland at the turn of the century suffered this malady (Meldorf 1900; Bertelsen 1905). A large number of cases (twenty-five) occurred as recently as 1949 in northern Greenland (Ehrstrom 1951). The condition has been compared to "break-off" which occurs in jet pilots who lose perception of reference points while flying at high altitudes (Flinn 1964; Gussow 1963). While the hunter waits quietly in the calm, reflecting sea, there develops a lowering in the level of consciousness brought on by the absence of external stimuli. As soon as this state of sensory deprivation is broken by rippling waves or a companion's voice, the hunter is able to orient himself. Severe headaches, urgency to urinate or defecate, and nausea are common immediate sequellae. Later on the individual may experience an increasing emotional lability and level of anxiety to the point of ruminating over morbid fears and overresponding to loud noises, dogs, etc., with extreme startle. Gussow (1963) in discussing Kayak phobia pointed out that the Eskimo characteristically tends to "give up" in situations perceived as intensely stressful, as opposed to trying new methods of coping. Drowning or giving up hunting seem to be the only effective alternatives to the unremitting anxiety. The fear of death by drowning is of constant concern to the Eskimo, and with good reason. Between 1901 and 1930 there were 1023 deaths by accident in Greenland; eighty percent were due to drowning and ninety-four percent of these were Kayak accidents (Bertelsen 1930).

Unlike the jet pilot, the Eskimo apparently prefers to suppress personal hardship and misfortune from himself and especially from others. He usually must keep feelings of pain and distress to himself, and thus cannot gain psychological support from the experiences of others. Developing the necessary defenses and coping mechanisms to personally deal with his anxiety is correspondingly hindered. If he attempted to discuss his difficulties with others, he would very likely be shamed by their joking laughter and ridicule. Anxiety and stress once started thus becomes chronic and ultimately leads to persistent anxiety states and interpersonal withdrawal.

Hermiting Behavior or Qivitoq

Interpersonal withdrawal to the point of actually leaving one's village was also frequently observed. Freuchen (1935) mentioned a young man who expressed his loneliness for his wife to other men while hunting. He was accordingly ridiculed and told "to stay at home and sew and care for the lamps, or employ your mouth for the talk of men." One man in the group decided to emphasize the predicament of the lamenter by taking his wife away from him. He was told that if he were lonely enough to want her back, he should figure out how to retrieve her. Overt aggression was not customarily expressed by the Eskimo. In past years, an angry man was considered a mad man, and among the Polar Eskimos such a person might be killed (Shackleton 1939:136). Thus, the young man withdrew and cried for three days. His own abducted wife laughed at him and chided him for his weakness. He then decided that he could no longer live with his people and went to live alone inland as a hermit. He became a *qivitoq*—a ghost who may never return home (cited in Gussow 1963:24). Rink (1875:45) described a *qivitoq*

> as a man who fled mankind and led a solitary life alone with nature generally in the interior of the country, obtained an enormous agility and became Nalussaerutok (to be aware of everything); learned to understand the speech of animals and acquired information about the world pillars. The reasons which led men to become qivitoq were being unfitly treated, or being merely scolded by kindred or housemates . . .

Suicide

Another method of withdrawal was offered through suicide. People in the prime of their lives whose relationships with members of their group had been threatened were candidates for suicide. There were several ways one's relationships might become threatened. One occurred when a person became socially or physically disabled and a hardship on the community. He would soon realize the growing dissatisfaction among his associates. The group would initially resort to teasing, joking, and ridiculing him. If these mechanisms failed to produce the desired changes, the group ceased all communication with him; even his friends and kin might not speak to him or look at him. Frequently relatives admonished the individual to the point of encouraging him to do away with himself. Rasmussen (1927) mentions a young man who was told by his foster father, "I wish you were dead! You are not worth the food you eat." And the young man took the words so seriously that he declared he indeed would not eat again. To make the suffering as brief as possible, the same young man lay down stark naked in the bare snow and was frozen to death. DePoncins (1941) told of a suicide in an older man which took place because of his being criticized about his ineffectual hunting ability by the younger men.

Usually, however, in cases which have been disabled through lameness and age, the group would be unlikely to be so openly uncongenial. However, such a person would often be quite aware of his liabilities and inwardly feel equally ostracized from the group.

Another way relationships were threatened was when they were terminated through death. Losing kinfolk and friends through death was an extreme hardship to the Eskimo. So much did he depend on others for his clothing, heat, comfort, and especially for his emotional sense of well being, that separation by death rendered a profound sense of loneliness. The surviving one often felt that somehow he had transgressed in his behavior, and had thus brought about his own abandonment. In fact, a man depended on his wife for so many aspects of living, that losing her through death or abandonment threatened the very basis of his sense of life. To be without her, meant to be without a life; one might as well be dead. The strong sense of jealously which exists in Eskimo men toward their wives' relationships with other men is to a certain extent based on this fundamental dependence. Many authors have noted that fights over women represented one of the main motives for male enmity and homicide (Birket-Smith 1959; Rasmussen 1932; Spencer 1959).

When it became apparent that a relationship might be irreconcilably lost through ostracism or through death of a loved one, suicide was considered. Often an individual would be assisted by others in committing suicide, since they desired to see him relieved of his suffering and his burden on the community (Hoebel 1941). It was often felt that one who suicided or died violently fared better in the hereafter than those who died through natural causes (Rasmussen 1931:144). Throwing oneself into the frigid sea water was one common method (Holm 1914). Another was to be abandoned to the elements on the Arctic tundra and perish by exposure (Weyer 1932:248).

Leighton and Hughes (1955) analyzed forty-four cases of successful suicide on St. Lawrence Island. They found that cases were usually old men, sometimes old women. Occasionally a younger person would hang, shoot, or stab himself with the assistance of relatives. The motivation for these suicides was predominantly suffering brought on by illness and loss of productivity and prestige. It was commonly believed that a suicide might save the life of another, usually a sick child. Thus, the behavior was considered altruistic and positively sanctioned accordingly. For the individual who had lost esteem and prestige, the act offered a way to regain social approval and enhance his status.

Recently, Balikci (1961) collected data on fifty suicide attempts which occurred in Pelly Bay over the past fifty years. Of these, thirty-five were successful, four abortive and eleven expressed suicidal intentions. Of the total, about twenty decided to commit suicide because of personal suffering, from illness or misfortune. Marital disharmony precipitated six decisions for suicide. Only four successfully took their lives because of old age and infirmity. Age distribution was as follows:

Number of Cases	Age
1	10
5	15-20
24	20-55
6	55-60
14	over 60

The suicide rate for the United States is about ten per 100,000. Balikci's figures for Pelly Bay indicate a rate of twenty times as great as this, and eight times the rate in Sweden, which according to statistics then available had the highest suicide rate in the world. Butler (1965) summarized the suicide statistics for the Canadian Arctic and concluded that the rate was considerably higher than the rate for Canada as a whole. However, he found that the rates for Eskimo suicide were not different than for other ethnic groups living in the same area, including whites. Statistics compiled by the US Public Health Service (Alaska Natives and Their Land 1968:20) and by the Bureau of Indian Health (1960-67) both show an incidence of about thirty per 100,000 for Alaska natives. These studies demonstrate an increasing incidence of suicide over the last ten years. Notably there has been a marked decline in suicide among the elderly, and an increase in suicide among the younger age groups during this period. Recently, Willis (1962) has demonstrated the relatively high incidence of mental disorder in general for the Eskimo of the Northwest Territories. He commented that the greater number of these were suicidal patients admitted to hospitals.

Psychiatric Admissions NW Territory (Rates per 100,000)

Year	Whites	Indians	Eskimos
1955	78	138	186
1956	116	228	370
1957	109	205	349
1958	98	202	288
1959	127	248	320
1960	133	219	328
1961	130	257	390

[Willis 1962:7]

Other authorities in Canada have considered suicide as one of the most characteristic manifestations of Eskimo psychiatric disorder (Willis and Martin 1962; Boag 1966; Vallee 1968:566). Nachman (1969) described an epidemic of suicide attempts which took place in Bethel during the winter and spring of 1968. Following one successful suicide, fifteen abortive attempts were made during the following sixty-day period by a number of others. Similar but milder "outbreaks" of suicidal behavior were described in Barrow and Kotzebue. Most of those cases were young women in their teens or early twenties who had experienced a rebuff or loss of friendship. Most attempted suicide by taking an overdose of a drug. Nachman (1969) emphasized the similarity between these seemingly impulsive, suicidal "fits" and the behavior seen during attacks of Arctic Hysteria.

The element common to Kayak phobia, hermiting behavior, and suicide is intentional social-psychological withdrawal. In each of these disorders the individual was presented with anxieties that could not be handled by group support. In fact, in most cases the anxieties were created by the critical nature of the Eskimo group itself. Being unable to express anger in open confrontation with the group left few psychological alternatives to the withdrawal. In *pibloktoq*, the individual is temporarily using the same withdrawal mechanisms. Rather than removing his physical being from the group by running away or killing himself, the person with Arctic Hysteria unconsciously takes his mind on a trip for a time, and forgets.

IV. The Epidemiology of the Arctic Hysterias and Other Mental Disorders

EPISODES OF BEHAVIOR resembling the Arctic Hysterias have been reported in Alaska. Several of these reports were included in the last chapter. The epidemiology of these behaviors, however, has not been established, thus posing several questions: What is the incidence and prevalence of this behavior? In what Alaskan ethnic groups is it seen? What demographic variables are associated with its occurrence?

In an attempt to clarify some of these problems, an epidemiological survey was made of the various mental disorders of Alaskan natives reported during the year of 1968. Arctic Hysterias, *pibloktoq*, and other terms used thus far are not, strictly speaking, part of medical and psychiatric nomenclature. Present day nosology would include these behaviors under the diagnostic category "conversion hysteria." Thus the overall survey of mental disorders was undertaken with particular focus on this diagnostic category.

Before outlining the methods and results of this survey, some discussion will be devoted to the development and present day status of the mental health care delivery system in Alaska. This will offer the reader some perspective on the data to be analyzed. In addition, since psychiatric diagnostic categories have rather precise referrents, an appendix to this chapter is offered to provide the nonmedical reader with some basic definitions (see Appendix B).

MENTAL HEALTH OF ALASKAN NATIVES BEFORE 1968

The Congressional Act of June 6, 1900, authorized the governor of the Territory of Alaska to make contracts for care and custody of "the insane," and in 1904 the Morningside Hospital of Portland, Oregon, received the contract and retained it until 1962. In 1949 the Department of the Interior required a report on mental health under Dr. Winfred Overholser. Morningside Hospital was surveyed for this report in 1954 by Thomas Parran, who published the following psychiatric data:

Psychiatric Caseload from Alaska:
Morningside Hospital, Portland
1953

Diagnosis	Per-cent of 350 cases
Psychoses	51.6%
Alcoholism	18.3%
Senile Psychosis	18.3%
Personality Disorders	6.6%
	(Parran 1954)

This committee concluded that the fundamental principle of contract care outside the territory was impractical, and recommended the construction of a modern mental hospital in Alaska, of not less than 350 beds. In 1956, the US Public Health Service survey team, which was authorized by Public Law 830 (Congress July 28, 1956) found that Morningside Hospital, because of its remoteness from Alaska, caused "difficulties and dissatisfactions." Vital contact with family and friend was lost to the hospitalized Eskimo, creating secondary psychiatric difficulties. They were held in hospitals perhaps longer than necessary to be certain they could return home to stay because of the great transportation expenses. Follow-up care was virtually impossible (Comprehensive Community Mental Health Planning 1965).

The Alaska Division of Mental Health finally began in 1952 with the opening of an outpatient clinic in Anchorage. In 1959 a clinic was established in Juneau and another in Fairbanks. Each of these clinics provided care for a large geographic area of Alaska. Presently, Fairbanks serves the entire northern half of the State; Anchorage the southern half; and Juneau the southeastern panhandle. In 1962 the Alaska Psychiatric Institute in Anchorage opened its 225 beds for the mentally disordered. While reducing the difficulties presented by the remoteness of Morningside Hospital, many natives, especially Eskimos, are still separated from friends and family, in some cases as much as 1000 miles, during their hospitalization. Recently the Division of Mental Health has initiated a policy of professional consultation in the more remote villages, which hopefully will reduce the necessity of many hospitalizations in Anchorage.

In addition to the State Divison of Mental Health, the US Public Health Service administers a mental health program. Usually the field hospitals are staffed by young medical doctors doing two years' duty with the US Public Health Service. In most cases these internships are attempting to fulfill their service obligations before beginning their residencies in a particular medical specialty. Thus their experience and expertise with psychiatric conditions is quite variable. This, of course, introduces the possibility that mental disorders at these field hospitals will be misdiagnosed. On the other hand, the USPHS has established a "psychiatric team" composed of a psychiatrist, a psychologist, and several social workers who provide ongoing consultation and treatment services to the field hospitals. In addition, they furnish the field physician the opportunity of more sophisticated diagnostic skills.

Recently the USPHS and the State agencies have integrated their programs of mental health care. The clinics of the State's Division of Mental Health provide consultation services to the Public Health Service field hospitals within their geographic region. In addition, the more severe, chronic psychiatric patients are often referred by Public Health Service physicians for treatment at the Alaska Psychiatric Institute.

MENTAL HEALTH OF ALASKA NATIVES IN 1968

During November 1969, 10,779 clinical records of Alaskan natives who had been treated for health problems the previous year were examined. The records were collected at the Arctic Health Research Institute at College, Alaska, and represented a coded record of all clinical cases treated at Public Health Field Hospitals in Alaska during 1968. They included 4106 at the Anchorage Hospital, 2548 in Bethel, 1483 at Mt. Edgecumbe, 704 at Tanana, 800 at Kotzebue, 817 at Kanakanak, and 321 at Barrow. Diagnosis was recorded according to the nomenclature used in the International Classification of Diseases (adopted 1962). The records were surveyed in terms of psychiatric diagnosis, place of occurrence and population size, and ethnic identity.

It is important to emphasize that morbidity statistics on true incidence and prevalence of mental disorders do not exist for the United States or any other country. The major obstacles to their development have been the absence of effective, standardized case finding methods capable of cross-cultural comparisons. In Alaska these problems are compounded by the diversity of ethnic groups and geographic isolation. Non-familiarity with English, with the usual questionnaire or interview survey formats, and built-in reluctance to discuss personal problems with outsiders further render overall population survey most difficult.

Although true morbidity statistics on mental disorders are lacking, systematic statistics are available on how clinics and mental health institutions are used by populations. These data represent the incidence and prevalence of treated mental disorders rather than the incidence and prevalence of the total occurrence of mental disorder. These figures are available for example from each state as well as for the US population as a whole.

The official population of Alaska is now 302,173 (1970 Census of Population). About 55,200 of this total are Alaskan natives. Population estimates for the major ethnic groups include the Eskimos—11,000 Innuit who live predominantly along the coast from Unalakeet north, and 17,000 Yuit who live along the coast south of this city; 6700 Athabascan Indians who inhabit interior Alaska predominantly along the riverbanks of the Yukon, Tanana, and Koyukuk; 12,000 Southeastern coast Indians including Tlingit, Tsimtsians, and Haida, and 6500 Aleuts who inhabit the Aleutian chain (Gazaway 1971). Because of the small size of these populations, results presented in the usual manner of rates per 100,000 should be interpreted with caution (see Table I).

TABLE I. INCIDENCE OF TREATED MENTAL DISORDERS
PER 100,000 OF EACH POPULATION SPECIFIED

	Native Alaskans 1968	Total Alaskans Treated in 1967*	U.S. Population Treated in 1967*
Neurosis	227	155.0	77.3
Psychophysiological	38	11	2.3
Psychosis	78	163.7	153.7
Personality Disorders	333	168.0	197.6
Other	107	402.1	301.1
Total	783	899.8	732.0

*Represents sum of inpatient and outpatient treatment in general and state hospitals (National Institute of Mental Health 1967).

During the year 1968, there were 432 native people who were treated for psychiatric disorder, rendering an incidence of 783 per 100,000 native population. This is not significantly higher than figures for the overall US population. The incidence rate for Alaskans in general is higher than the US population. However, native people of the state are treated less frequently than whites for psychiatric conditions perhaps because most mental health facilities are located in urban areas and are thus more available to the predominant white population of these areas. Noteworthy, however, is the distribution of types of mental disorder among these populations. The pattern of mental disorders for Alaskans in general differs only slightly from the pattern presented by the overall US population. However, the pattern for native Alaskans varies from them in several interesting respects.

Neurosis and personality disorders are treated more frequently in Alaskan natives than in the general white, western population of Alaska and other states in the US. Table II indicates that depressive neurosis, anxiety, and alcoholism account for a large portion of this discrepancy. It is also noteworthy that psychosis is seen less frequently among the Alaskan natives. The high incidence of alcoholism may be responsible for this since there may be many psychotic individuals who because of their severe mental disorder drink large amounts of alcohol, and present themselves for treatment of alcoholism, the underlying psychotic process going unrecognized. This situation is further suggested by the analysis of patterns of mental disorder according to the major Alaskan native groups (Tables III and IV).

Overall incidence of treated mental disorder differed significantly among the major ethnic groups. Yuit Eskimos, Athabascan Indians, and Southeastern Indians shared higher than average rates. Innuit Eskimos and Aleuts had lower than average rates. This may be accounted for in part by the remoteness of most Innuit and Aleut communities from psychiatric facilities.

TABLE II. MENTAL DISORDERS OF THE ALASKAN NATIVE, 1968

Diagnosis	N	Percent of Total Mental Disorders	Incidence per 100,000 Native Alaskans
Depression	54	12.5	94
Conversion Hysteria	8	2	15
Anxiety Neurosis	57	13	103
Neurosis (Other)	9	2	15
Psychophysiological Disorders	21	5	38
Alcoholism	165	38	299
Paranoid Personality	19	4	34
Paranoid Schizophrenia	13	3	24
Acute Undifferentiated	6	1.4	11
Chronic Undifferentiated	14	3	24
Other	10	2	18
Schizophrenia Total*	43	10	78
Epilepsy	48	11	86
Miscellaneous	4	—	—
Total	432	100	783

*Computed separate from sub-types.

Alcoholism

Alcoholism accounts for a major portion of mental disorders in all ethnic groups, however, its occurrence seems especially high among the Athabascans and Aleuts. Noteworthy is the observation that these groups are also treated less frequently for schizophrenia which is a major psychosis.

Availability of alcohol, of course, depends to a large extent on a cash economy, and some degree of breakdown in traditional social structures. Larger villages of 900-2500 (native people of Alaska do not live on reservations, but in discrete, scattered communities termed by them and the State and Federal Governments "villages") and urban areas offer such a situation. Yuit Eskimos, Athabascans, and Southeastern Indians account for the majority of natives living in white, urban areas, and suffer a high incidence of alcoholism.

TABLE III. INCIDENCE OF TREATED MENTAL DISORDERS PER 100,000 OF EACH MAJOR ALASKAN ETHNIC GROUP

	N	Innuit	Yuit	Aleut	Athabascan	Southeastern Indians	Overall Native Incidence	χ^2, p
Depression	54	127	200	0	30	33	94	
Conversion Hysteria	8	63	6	0	0	0	15	33.722, <.005
Anxiety Neurosis	57	82	171	46	119	67	103	11.823, .025, > P > .01
Neurosis (Other)	9	10	42	0	0	17	15	
Psychophysiological Disorders	21	0	42	16	0	117	38	25.043, <.005
Alcoholism	165	200	371	446	567	200	299	40.671, <.005
Paranoid Personality	19	0	21	16	0	158	34	
Paranoid Schizophrenia	13	19	41	16	0	25	24	—
Acute Undifferentiated	6	0	24	0	0	17	11	—
Chronic Undifferentiated	14	0	63	0	0	25	24	—
Schizophrenia (Other)	10	27	24	0	15	17	18	—
Schizophrenia Total	43	45	156	16	15	83	78	21.151, <.005
Epilepsy	48	19	77	31	180	117	86	
Miscellaneous	4	—	—	—	—	—	—	
Total Incidence	432	555	959	562	898	833	783	23.706, <.005
N/Population		61/11,000	164/17,000	37/6,500	60/6,700	100/1,200	432/55,200	

TABLE IV. MENTAL DISORDERS PER 100 PATIENTS OF EACH MAJOR ALASKAN ETHNIC GROUP

	N	Innuit	Yuit	Aleut	Atha-bascan	South-eastern	Total
Number of patients in each group		61	164	37	60	100	432
Depression	54	23	21	0	3	4	12.5
Conversion Hysteria	8	12	2	0	0	0	2
Anxiety Neurosis	57	15	18	8	13	8	13
Neurosis (Other)	9	2	4	0	0	2	2
Psychophysiological Disorders	21	0	4	3	0	14	5
Alcoholism	165	35	38	79	62	24	38
Paranoid Personality	19	0	2	3	0	19	4
Paranoid Schizophrenia	13	3	4	3	0	3	3
Acute Undifferentiated	6	0	3	0	0	2	14
Chronic Undifferentiated	14	0	2	0	0	3	3
Schizophrenia (Other)	10	5	3	0	2	2	2
Schizophrenia Total	43	8	12	3	2	10	10
Epilepsy	48	3	9	5	20	19	11
Total	432	100	100	100	100	100	100

Paranoid Personality Disorder

The incidence of paranoid personality disorder is significantly higher among Southeastern Indians. Reasons for this may be more culture bound and traditional. Benedict (1934) outlined in detail a social and personality profile of the Kwakiut Indians who are related to the Southeastern Alaskan peoples. In this outline she stressed the adaptive interplay between the favored paranoid personality type and the individualistic and competitive values originally stressed by these societies. It is also noteworthy, however, that these disorders occurred with greatest frequency in Southeastern Indians who lived in the larger urban areas in greatest contact with the white world.

Depression and Hysterical Neurosis

Overt depression was seen with highest frequency among the Eskimo. This is possibly a reflection of the fact that both Innuit Eskimos account for the majority of large (900-2500) native villages in Alaska (Bethel, Nome, Kotzebue, and Barrow). Table V indicates that the majority of cases of depression occurred in the larger villages. Life in the larger villages differs from life in the smaller villages in several respects. Larger villages are in greater contact with Western society. Many white people live in these villages and work at government facilities established there. The facilities around Barrow, for example, include the Naval Arctic Research Laboratory, a Distant Early Warning Station, a Bureau of Indian Affairs Elementary and Junior High School, a US Public Health Service Hospital, a municipal airport, many dry goods stores and hotels, several churches, state health and welfare representatives, and many others. Such large populations, of course, can no longer depend on traditional hunting subsistence methods; instead they become dependent on the available cash economy brought in through the various government and commercial agencies in the form of jobs and welfare.

TABLE V. TREATED MENTAL DISORDERS ACCORDING TO VILLAGE SIZE

	Total 55,200	Villages 500 = 50.5% total	Villages 500-900 = 6.5% total	Villages 900 = 19% total	Predominantly Caucasian Towns and Cities	
Depression	54	29	2	65	4	100
Conversion Hysteria	8	88	0	12	0	100
Anxiety Neurosis	57	53	2	5	40	100
Neurosis (Other)	9	44	0	44	11	100
Psychophysiological Disorders	21	76	0	5	19	100
Alcoholism	165	14	0	16	70	100
Paranoid Personality	19	5	0	0	95	100
Paranoid Schizophrenia	13	62	33	15	0	100
Acute Undifferentiated	6	67	16	0	16	100
Chronic Undifferentiated	14	65	15	15	5	100
Schizophrenia (Other)	10	40	30	10	20	100
Schizophrenia Total	43	58	23	12	7	100
Epilepsy	48	39	6	8	47	100
Miscellaneous	4	—	—	—	—	—
Total	432	33%	5%	18%	44%	100%

The larger villages have native governing bodies and well-defined rules and regulations which are enforced by constables and the government courts; in smaller villages such explicit defining of the law is generally unnecessary since social control is achieved personally through scrutiny during the daily rounds of visiting. In the larger village, such daily face-to-face contact becomes impossible. Here social control is achieved through adherence to rules. Self-esteem in this case is lowered by falling short of these rules generating guilt, and guilt is considered a psychological concomitant of depression (Piers and Singer 1953).

Many rules and standards are introduced to the Alaskan villages from sources outside his own culture. Experience in Western oriented schools, churches, and government agencies often creates in the native expectations for himself which he feels unable to meet. This situation, of course, generates low self-esteem and manifestations of depression.

In contrast, several authors (Ehrstrom 1951; Parker 1962) have suggested that life in the smaller, more traditional Eskimo village generated an entirely different type of psychology. Such small populations permit daily face-to-face personal contacts for everyone. Daily face-to-face contact allows the traditional Eskimo practices of social control, i.e., ridicule, joking and gossip to be practiced (Briggs 1971). These mechanisms of social control generate shame and rigid conformity to group norms. Hysterical conversion provides a way for the individual in such a situation to express his conflicts without having to assume responsibility for his behavior. In fact, Ehrstrom (1951) and Parker (1962) reported that in small, tradition-oriented Eskimo societies, stress resulting in mental disorder is commonly expressed according to hysterical mechanisms. Our figures indicate that when conversion hysteria occurs it is most likely to be seen in villages with population below 500 people, which are basically the more tradition-oriented Eskimo villages. In the past, when most Eskimos lived in such settlements, the condition may have been more common than today. Recent shifts in Eskimo settlement patterns and increasing contact with the Western world has effectively changed the configuration of traditional Eskimo life, and in so doing has altered psychological coping mechanisms and patterns of psychology. These trends will be the subject of the next section of this chapter.

Psychophysiological Disorders and Hysterical Neurosis

The Southeastern Alaskan Indian groups presented the greatest incidence of psychophysiological disorders. Disorders most commonly involved the gastrointestinal and cardiovascular systems. Some authorities have felt that there is an inverse relationship between the incidence of psychophysiological disorders and hysterical neurosis (Ehrstrom 1951; Parker 1962:78). It is proposed that in changing societies in contact with the Western world one can rarely rely on traditional behaviors in coping with life's problems. New decisions affecting one's life must be made daily in a frequently changing environmental and social world. The individual no longer can fall back on the old ways or the old people in handling problems of life such as what to study in school, what to do at work, where to live, whom to marry, what religion to follow, etc. This responsibility for new decisions in an ever-changing environment is thought to be extremely stressful in the psychological and physiological sense. Chronic stress ultimately is expressed in sympathetic-parasympathetic imbalance in certain organs innervated by the autonomic nervous system. The imbalance results in malfunctions of the involved system and the appearance of psychophysiological diseases. It is noteworthy that the Southeastern Alaskan Indian groups have had comparatively longer and more intensive contact with the Western world than any other native group in Alaska, and now suffer the highest incidence of psychophysiological disorders. It is further suggested that while change-oriented societies express conflict through psycho-physiological mechanisms, the more tradition-oriented societies express conflict through hysterical mechanisms. The rationale for the proposal is as follows: in contrast to the rapidly changing society, in the small tradition-oriented society, one relies primarily upon prescribed means of coping with life's problems. In Eskimo groups of this type, deviance from traditional behavior is subject to considerable ridicule and gossip. The deviant is shamed into conformity. When stresses arise that cannot be satisfactorily handled through the traditional channels, the individual is faced with handling his conflicts personally. However, he cannot in most cases express his feelings, especially anger, openly without subjecting himself to ridicule. The alternative is the expression of the conflict without the individual consciously realizing the purpose of his behavior. Thus the hysterical symptom is developed, and may involve destructive behavior with amnesia for the event, paralysis of limbs, phobias, and a myriad of other somatic possibilities. Such symptoms have been described in attacks of *pibloktoq* or Arctic Hysteria. Our data indicate that conversion hysteria is limited to the Eskimo groups, and occurs predominantly in the Innuit (see Tables III and IV).

RECENT SHIFTS IN ALASKAN NATIVE POPULATION

During the last century, human population has increased dramatically the world over. Reasons for this increase are multiple and undoubtedly include improved prenatal and parturition care, lowered infant mortality rates, improved medical care, increases in fertility, and increased average life span. These factors and others have also affected profound changes in the Alaskan native population in recent years. Katz and Foulks (1971) have recently demonstrated how many of these recent changes have brought a new type of living to the present-day Eskimo and Indian. It is reasonable to assume that changes of such magnitude would create unique stresses and alter long established patterns of behavior.

In 1967 the Federal Field Committee, established to assess the effects of the Great Alaskan Earthquake of the early 1960s, did a comprehensive study on the natives and the land. This group collected population statistics for predominantly native villages in 1950 and in 1967. These population statistics are most useful·in analysis of the trends and patterns of the shifts from small subsistence-oriented villages to considerably larger and predominately native population centers with a cash based economy.

Figure 1 is a plot of the distribution of population by number of villages and village size on the lower half for 1950 and 1967. This figure demonstrates the change in the number of villages at various sizes and simultaneously the distribution of population within them. In so doing we can describe the characteristics of the small village in 1950 and the shift to larger villages in 1967 while taking note of the overall growth in native population throughout the state of Alaska. There are several striking features about the pattern of population distribution in 1950. First is the fact that the greatest number of villages contained less than 100 people although the 100-200 population size village contained the most people. One rather direct explanation of this large number of small villages is the problem of limited resources in practicing a subsistence economy with little outside help in the way of cash, education and/or medical care. In other words, the combination of limited exploitation of resources (essentially this means carrying out traditional native hunting and fishing technology with the added help of guns, etc.) with high mortality and morbidity rates effectively limited the size of most native villages. Life essentially fit the more traditional patterns.

At the upper end of village size in 1950 only two villages had a population about 900. By 1967, several important intervening variables occurred which markedly shifted the population pattern. There was an overall dramatic decrease in neonatal deaths (which is continuing to decline due to the widespread introduction of public health facilities). The latter also led to a dramatic decrease in the early 1950s in the mortality rates from TB with the widespread use of ameliorative drugs. There was an overall increase in the rate of welfare and education through the auspices of the Bureau of Indian Affairs. This led to greater availability of cash and a greater desire for better education of children in the larger BIA schools.

The overall effect of these outside health, welfare, and economic benefits especially available in the larger villages led to a very rapid development of these towns. Thus, relatively great waves of migrants from the smaller villages moved to larger villages which offered cash employment, medical benefits, educational facilities, and an opportunity to live with relatives in a predominately native village.

Table VI summarizes these movements according to various divisions of population size. From 1950 to 1967, villages with less than 500 still grew considerably, but relative to the total population they declined in size. This growth was probably due mostly to decreases in mortality with little or

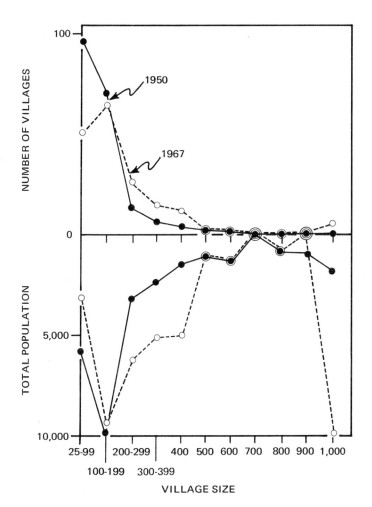

Figure 1. Growth of predominately native villages in Alaska, by number, size, and total population.

TABLE VI. ALASKAN NATIVE POPULATION GROWTH BY VILLAGE SIZE*

	less than 500		500-900		900-2500	
	Total Population	% of Total	Total Population	% of Total	Total Population	% of Total
1950	22,990	79.1%	3,231	11.1%	2,827	9.7%
1967	28,836	68.7%	3,176	7.6%	9,951	23.7%
percent growth 1950-67	+25.4%	−10.4%	−1.7%	−3.5%	+252.0%	+14.0%

*Katz 1971

TABLE VII. INCIDENCE OF TREATED MENTAL DISORDER ACCORDING TO VILLAGE SIZE PER 100,000 IN POPULATION SPECIFIED

	N	Villages <500	Villages 500-900	Villages >900	Predominantly Caucasian Cities	Total Incidence	X^2	p
	414	27,876	3,176	10,488	13,248			
Depression	53	57	—	335	14	94	70.09	$<.005$
Conversion Hysteria	8	26	—	7	0	15	—	
Anxiety Neurosis	56	109	—	30	172	103	11.310	$<.005$
Neurosis (Other)	9	10	—	37	29	15	—	
Psychophysiological Disorders	21	57	—	7	—	38	4.771	$.1>p>.05$
Alcoholism	165	83	—	283	889	299	182.445	$<.005$
Paranoid Personality	23	5	—	0	172	34	—	
Paranoid Schizophrenia	31	31	—	15	0	24		
Acute Undifferentiated	5	10	—	0	7	11		
Chronic Undifferentiated	12	31	—	15	7	24		
Schizophrenia (Other)	7	10	—	7	14	18		
Schizophrenia Total	34	52	—	52	29	78	—	
Epilepsy	45	62	—	37	172	86	15.826	$<.05$
Total Incidence	414	517	—	744	1434	783	107.124	$<.005$

no shift in fertility. In the intermediate sized villages (500-900), there was a decrease in both absolute numbers and a decrease in percentage of the total population. This stagnation problem reflects a status where the villages have grown to be too large to be supported by the local ecosystem with a subsistence economic base and too small to be attractive to migration. However, it is noteworthy that in 1950 seven villages out of this group were destined to grow into the greater than 900 category. Finally, at the greater than 900 size village population, a dramatic increase in population took place over the interval of seventeen years. There was approximately a 250% increase in the number of people in villages of this size and an overall increase to 23.7% of all natives living in predominately native villages, which means a 14% increase in total native population living in this kind of village in seventeen years. Undoubtedly, this is a large migrant population attracted to a new center of activity for jobs, education and medical care. The greater size of these communities requires a more complex social organization with a mayor, a town council, a constable and various other institutions formerly not always part of the smaller more tradition-oriented villages. Contact with Western products and ways of life is also enhanced bringing about more changes in life style.

Finally, it should be noted that significant migration into the predominately white urban areas of Alaska such as Anchorage, Juneau, and Fairbanks has created still another unique category of native settlement with corresponding patterns of mental disorder. It is estimated that 2000 Yupiat and 900 Innupiat Eskimos, 1575 Athabascans, and 200 Tlingit Indians presently live in Anchorage. In Fairbanks there are 1020 Athabascan Indians and about 800 Eskimos (Gazaway 1971).

TABLE VIII. MENTAL DISORDERS ACCORDING TO
TOTAL TREATED FROM EACH CATEGORY OF VILLAGE SIZE

	Total Pop. 55,200	Villages < 500 50.5% total	Villages < 900 19% total	Predominantly Caucasian Towns/Cities 24% total
Depression	54	11%	45%	1%
Conversion Hysteria	8	5%	1%	0%
Anxiety Neurosis	57	21%	4%	12%
Neurosis (Other)	9	2%	5%	0.5%
Psychophysiological Disorders	21	11%	1%	2%
Alcoholism	165	16%	32%	62%
Paranoid Personality	19	1%	0%	12%
Paranoid Schizophrenia	13	6%	2%	0%
Acute Undifferentiated	6	2%	0%	0.5%
Chronic Undifferentiated	14	6%	2%	0.5%
Schizophrenia (Other)	10	2%	1%	1%
Schizophrenia Total	43	10%	7%	2%
Epilepsy	48	12%	5%	12%
Miscellaneous	4	—	—	—
Total %	—	100	100	100
Total N	432	144	78	190

POPULATION SIZE AND MENTAL DISORDER

Table VII relates the relative contribution of each diagnostic category to the total mental disorders treated from each column of village size.

The commonest mental disorders treated in smaller villages (<500) are anxiety neuroses. The distribution of mental disorders, in villages of this size, is remarkably uniform. In the larger villages, however, another pattern emerges. Depression is by far the most frequently seen disorder. Factors responsible for this dramatic increase in the larger villages have already been discussed. Alcoholoism is also on the increase in the larger villages. These two mental disorders represent the major mental health problems presented by these rapidly expandinging villages.

The predominately Caucasian towns and cities present an even more disproportionate increase in alcoholism. This disorder represents sixty-two percent of all types of mental disorders in Alaskan natives treated in the urban areas.

Table VIII indicates that the rapid changes which have occurred in the larger villages and in native populations in urban areas have resulted in increasing incidences of mental disorder. The overt incidence of mental disorder among Alaskan natives living in predominately western towns is almost three times the incidence in the smaller villages. Anxiety neurosis and alcoholism are seen to be significantly correlated with native populations living in urban areas. The incidence of alcoholism alone in urban areas of Alaska actually exceeds the combined incidence for every other mental disorder in Alaska and the other states.

Migration has been implicated as a contributor to psychopathology (Brody 1970). In addition, Hippler (1969) has recently summarized the particular problems of the Alaskan native who migrates to the predominantly white urban areas. Difficulties in gaining employment, racial discrimination, prejudice, inadequate educational opportunities, limited competence in English, and patronizing government agents were felt to contribute significantly to confusion, loneliness, despair, and alienation, which resulted in alcoholism and other mental disorders.

There are also changes in the dietary habits of villagers who migrate to urban areas. Resultant deficiencies of protein, magnesium, and other essential foods may place additional burdens on the physiological functioning of the central nervous system thus contributing to mental disorder.

V. The Antiquity of the North Alaskan Eskimo: A Foundation for the Arctic Hysterias

THE ARCTIC HYSTERIAS are relatively rare among the various mental disorders of present-day circumpolar peoples. It is probably fair to speculate from reviewing the literature that the condition was far more common in times past. Our survey of mental disorders among Alaskan natives in 1968 indicated that Arctic Hysteria-like behavior was restricted to the northern Eskimo groups who lived predominantly in the smaller villages.

After completion of this survey, our investigation focused on several villages in north Alaska. Residence was established through the various seasons of the year. Observations were collected and recorded in daily field notes regarding the social interactions and ways of life followed by these people. More detailed investigations were conducted on cases of Arctic Hysteria-like behavior which occurred during the year's fieldwork. The results of this aspect of our fieldwork will be presented in this and the following chapter.

The historical-cultural component of our study is considered fundamental to the overall synthetic approach proposed in this study. This chapter will, therefore, introduce the North Alaskan Eskimos and examine in detail their cultural history.

ARCHEOLOGICAL RECONSTRUCTION

This section will summarize primarily the archeological record and certain historical documents as they pertain to the people of North Alaska. In doing so, an attempt will be made to clarify the cultural and genetic relationships of these people to other groups also living in the arctic such as Indians, Aleuts, Siberian, and other Eskimo populations. Arctic people have much in common culturally and historically. In addition, all are faced with common problems of adapting to the arctic environment. The commonalities and relationship among arctic people which contributed to the near universal circumpolar syndrome of the Arctic Hysterias may provide insights into the etiological factors involved.

The North Alaskan Eskimos inhabit primarily six villages on the coast of the Arctic Ocean. Barrow, the largest village, is situated on the northern most point of Alaska about 70° 45′ North and 159° 30′ West. Wainwright, Point Lay, Point Hope, and Kivalina extend along the coast west of Barrow, and Kaktovik is situated on Barter Island east of Barrow.

Some authors have pointed out cultural differences between the Arctic coast, whale hunting Eskimos or *Tareumiut*, and the more inland Eskimos of the Brooks Range, the *Nunamiut*, who subsisted primarily from hunting Caribou (Oswalt 1967). Many of these differences indicate long, separate historical traditions in each area (Bandi 1969:130). In the case of the present-day Eskimos of the Arctic coast, it is not certain that they originated purely from either one or the other of these traditions. In the nineteenth century, white whalers with their new diseases decimated the original *Tareumiut* population of North Alaska, as shown by the figures of Jackson (1891:5).

Place	Population		
	1828	1863	1890
Pt. Barrow	1000	309	100
Pt. Franklin	Large	?	0
Pt. Hope	2000	?	350

Rainey (1941:10) believed that the Eskimo population from Kotzebue to Demarcation Pt. numbered about 10,000 in 1850 but was reduced to 3000 by 1900, due to disease and shortage of game. Jenness (1968:10) felt that disease and alcohol-promoted disorders introduced by the whalers, reduced the North Alaskan Eskimo population to barely one-tenth of its earlier number. The aboriginal population of the Wainwright area was counted in 1882 by Lieutenant Ray (cited in Milan 1964:20):

Wainwright Inlet 10	families	. . . .	80 people
SW of Pt. Belcher 8	families	. . . .	50 people
Cape Smythe 23	families	. . . . .	150 people

At this same period there existed a relatively large settlement of *Nunamiut* nearby on the Utukok River. According to Larsen and Rainey (1948:31), they may have numbered 800 or more. These were people who hunted caribou and fished along the upper Utukok River and occasionally came to the Arctic coast for trading and sea mammal hunting. During the recent past, many of them have apparently settled on the coast. Many Arctic coast Eskimos including one of our subjects with Arctic Hysteria-like behavior were born in inland camps, and most at least acknowledge the *Nunamiut* as their ancestors (Milan 1964:3).

Contact and exchanges between the coastal and inland Eskimos of North Alaska have probably been very extensive for many centuries. Giddings, in fact, suggested that the term "Arctic Woodland Culture" be given to each developmental phase of the inland culture which corresponds to a respective development of coastal culture (Bandi 1969:127). Linguistic evidence also verifies that contact between *Nunamiut* and *Tareumiut* has been intense and of long duration. Hirsh (159:834) reported no dialect differences between the inland and coastal groups.

Finally, it is concluded by Spencer (1959:454) that

The Inland maritime dichotomy represents not one system which evolves into another, but rather two specialized kinds of developments in the domain of a common culture. When compared, it has been established that the two groups did not differ from each other except in the ways of making a living . . . both groups stand side by side in respect to weapon assemblage, clothing, the house types, social organization, religious and ceremonial life, shamanism, and world vein. The conclusion is that here are two interdependent ecological variations on a primary cultural theme.

Birnirk

About one-half mile northeast of Barrow are sixteen mounds arranged in three rows running parallel to the coast of the Arctic Ocean. These mounds represent the refuse from long settlement and the continuous construction of new buildings on the site of older ones. Stefanson (1914), recognizing the antiquity of the place, termed it the Birnirk culture. Systematic investigations were made of this site in 1932 by James Ford (1959). The Birnirk mounds contained many rectangular, semisubterranean houses built of driftwood and whale bones, and covered with sod. The population hunted seal, walrus, whale, and caribou. They used dog, umiaks (large skin boats), and kayaks. The people of Birnirk made pottery of two types: saucer-like seal oil lamps and cooking pots with vertical sides tapering to a conical-shaped bottom, terminating in a point. These vessels were frequently decorated with curvilinear designs. Birnirk sites have also been found southwest of Barrow, at Kugusgaruk, and at Pt. Belcher (Bandi 1969:121). On the bases of finds in these complexes, Ford has shown a gradual development took place from Birnirk culture to Thule culture, an Eskimo culture phase preceding the modern period. Birnirk culture dates to the period AD 500-900 by radiocarbon analyses (Bandi 1969:121), and is felt to be derived from a culture which Larsen and Rainey (1948) discovered at Pt. Hope and termed Ipiutak. This Pt. Hope site revealed the sequence

$$\text{Ipiutak} \longrightarrow \text{Birnirk} \longrightarrow \text{Western Thule} \longrightarrow \text{Tigara} \longrightarrow \text{modern}$$

paralleling Ford's conclusions regarding the sites around Barrow.

Antecedents of Birnirk

Ipiutak culture has been dated to about the second century AD (Bandi 1969:114). Certain unique burials at the Ipiutak site are believed to be a special class of persons, probably shamans (Larsen and Rainey 1948), indicating the great antiquity of this institution in Eskimo tradition. Shamanism is of special interest to this thesis since its relation to the Arctic Hysterias has been suggested by many authorities. In addition, one of our subjects with Arctic Hysteria-like behavior was influenced profoundly by this tradition. The Ipiutak burials of this special class of person were surface graves, perhaps originally enclosed in a log frame. A particular characteristic of these surface burials was the presence of numerous peculiarly carved forms of ivory. Some were openwork carvings looking like twisted rope and of very high quality. Others were fantastic animal figures, either unidentifiable or reminiscent of reptiles. Larsen and Rainey believed that these were attached to clothing around the shoulders, which they pointed out was frequently the case among the Tungus shamans of Siberia. These Ipiutak shamanistic art forms strongly resemble those that occurred in the Scytho-Siberian styles between 900-200 BC in the region of the Black Sea to Northern Shang China, and in part those of even earlier date, in the LaTene style of the late Iron Age in Central Europe (Bandi 1969:112). The motifs have also been manifest to the present day, in representations of evil spirits known as Tupilak carved by Eskimos in Angmagssalik, Greenland (Holm 1914:74). A few graves were found with artificial ivory eyeballs set into the skull's eye sockets, and, in addition, one with small sculptured ivory nose plugs. Another ivory carving is a mouth-cover representing lips which are sewn together. It is felt that these practices expressed the belief that the body openings had to be closed to prevent the molesting of the corpse by intrusive evil spirits. (Bandi 1969:110).

Ultimate Origins

The precedents of these Northern Alaskan Eskimo complexes have been traced ultimately by archeological and linguistic analysis (Dumond 1965) to a migration of Arctic peoples from Siberia over the Bering land bridge during the last phase of the Neopleistocene and early Holocene, about 10-13,000 years BC. Bandi (1969:33) states,

> An ever-increasing number of clues suggest that an ethnic group, thought to be of Arctic-Mongoloid stock, crossed the land bridge, infiltrated Alaska, and then advanced fairly rapidly further eastward through the Canadian Arctic as far as Greenland. We can hardly go wrong in associating the American Epi Gravettian, which has a tendency in favor of small implements, with the origins of Eskimo culture and in surmising that its representatives were ancestors of the Eskimos.

Larsen and Rainey (1948) favored the Eskimo's originating from the Ob River lowlands, because of the diffusion of such artifacts as round-bottom pots with checkerboard design and flint chipping; there is increasing evidence that the more probable area of immediate origin is the Pacific coast. The Eskimo skin boat, toggle harpoon, atlatl, blubber lamp, slate hunting knife, harpoon blade, and ulu are not generally seen in the North Asia inland coasts, but are found commonly around the Pacific coast to Korea. Laughlin (1963) postulates that during the time of the land bridge a series of contiguous, but partially isolated, groups of undifferentiated Mongoloids of a continuous cultural horizon, occupied the coasts from Hokkaido to southern Alaska. The site on Anagula Island at the tip of the Alaskan Peninsula complex there containing end-shaped burin, thick microblade, and core industry has a radiocarbon date in excess of 3000 years BC, and has been linked on the one hand with the microblade industries at Sakkotsu, Hokkaido, and with the Araya site in Honshu, and the Budun site in Siberia, which have been dated at 7-11,000 BC. On the other hand, Anangula not only has local continuities, but also has been considered a precursor industry to the Arctic Small Tool, or American Epi Gravettian. (See Figure 2.)

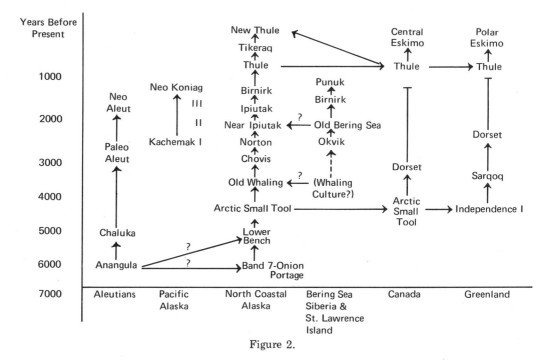

Figure 2.

LINGUISTIC AFFINITIES

Eskimos today are a people who reflect a remarkable degree of linguistic, racial, and cultural homogeneity. The people of North Alaska speak Inupiat which is mutually intelligible from the area of Unalakleet, across North Alaska, Arctic Canada, to eastern Greenland. The other related Eskimo language, Yupik, is spoken by people south of Unalakleet to Prince William Sound, and Kodiak Island. The Eskimos on St. Lawrence Island and in Siberia also speak a dialect of Yupik. Glottochronological analysis of Inupik and Yupik indicates the period of their separation to be sometime around AD 1000 (Collins 1954; Hirsh 1954; Dumond 1965), roughly coinciding with the spread of Thule culture from Seward Peninsula eastward to Greenland.

Using lexicostatistics and archeological evidence, Dumond (1965) concluded the following:

(a) The Chukotan language phylum, presently including Chuckchee, Koryak, and Kamchodal of northeastern Siberia, separated from Protoeskaleut around 8000 BP, roughly coinciding with the archeological evidence of a migration over the Bering Land Bridge by carriers of the American EpiGravettian culture.

(b) Speakers of Protoeskaleut lived before 6000 BP and were perhaps related to those people whose remains are represented in Anangula Island and perhaps Band 7 at Onion Portage.

(c) They were linguistic ancestors to both the people of the Chaluka-Aleut tradition and the people of the Arctic Small Tool tradition.

(d) Carriers of the Arctic Small Tool tradition, spread across the American Arctic to Greenland by 4000 BP. In the west they were ancestral to the people of the Norton Horizon; in the east, to the Dorset people whose language has not survived.

(e) The Norton people spread from the Alaskan Peninsula to the MacKenzie by 2000 BP and were the linguistic ancestors to both modern Yupik.

(f) Yupik speakers differentiated into two sub-dialects from 2000-1000 BP because of stationary living and relative isolation from each other: a mainland dialect from the Alaskan

Peninsula to St. Michaels; another on Nunivak Island.

(g) By 1000 BP, a group of mainland speakers migrated to the Pacific coast. Their disconnection created a third Yupik dialect, Pacific coast.

(h) People of the Thule culture spread Inupik speech across northern North America around 1000 BP.

This linguistic evidence, added to what we have already discussed concerning the archeological evidence, provides a consistent and inclusive explanation for the linguistic and cultural variations found in the present-day Eskimo and Aleut. As seen above, there are five major groups: the Aleut, who have developed in relative linguistic and cultural isolation for 6000 years; the Yupik-Nunivaks and the Yupik Mainlanders, for 2000 years; the Yupik-Pacific, for 1000 years; and the Inupik, who may have been influenced linguistically, culturally, and even genetically by the Ipiutak and later in Canada by Dorset peoples.

GENERAL ASPECTS OF ESKIMO CULTURE

A degree of cultural homogeneity has also existed between Eskimo groups. Most of the Arctic coast has at least five months in which the mean daily maximum temperature is below freezing, maintaining a condition of frozen ice surface. The Eskimo virtually monopolizes these North American coasts, with the exception of southern Hudson Bay. Coastal regions whose mean annual temperature is above thirty-five degrees are occupied by Aleuts and Indians. The only Eskimos living along such warmer coasts are to be found along the Gulf of Alaska.

The reliance on areas which have at least five months of frozen coastal waters is perhaps based on the fact that many Eskimos subsist on hunting sea mammals from shelf ice, and especially in the winter, depend on such activities as their major winter source of food, heat and clothing. The frozen coast allows easy access to the seals for example who either lie on top of the ice or come to the surface through breathing holes. Seal and caribou hides provided warm, efficient clothing. Seal blubber was burned for heat and light in special flat bowl-shaped lamps. Pursuit of the seal and caribou required the use of the dog sled and the quickly constructed temporary snow shelters: in Canada the snow igloo. Dependence on a supply of game was so great during the winter months that much elaborate ritual and taboo concerning proper methods to hunt, to cut the carcass, to distribute the meat, etc., was followed in order to insure the good will of the animal's spirit, that it might return again in the future with another animal body asking to be killed. Festivals were held in honor of the hunters or in honor of the animal killed including the Bladder Festivals for seal, and Nulaktuk for the whale.

Social organization was also to a certain extent dictated by the hunting economy. There was an absolute division of labor between men and women. Males hunted and prepared hunting equipment. Females utilized the animal's carcass completely, in preparing food, tanning and sewing the hides into clothing, and using the fat in tending the household lamp. The average Eskimo hunter provided only enough meat to feed himself, his wife and two to four children. Only in rare cases could anyone afford to keep more than one wife, more than four children, or more than his own nuclear family. Male children were favored because of their potential capacity for future food providing. Infanticide was often practiced on female children.

Hunting was often a solitary procedure. In a few instances, two men might cooperate in the hunt. But more than two was usually a hindrance and a waste of time for those looking on, when they could be out catching game for themselves.

In some special instances, however, Eskimos cooperated in large hunting enterprises. Caribou were often herded into funnel-shaped stone enclosures which contained the animals while a number of hunters butchered them. On other occasions caribou were herded into a stream or lake where they could be easily hunted by men in boats. The Eskimos of northwest Alaska also hunted whales, which required elaborate planning and cooperation between members of the whaling crew and the Umealik, the leader of the hunt and provider of supplies. In spite of these exceptions, it was generally the case that each man was responsible for his own hunting and his own family. In times of need, however, sharing was universally practiced. Such an individualistic situation did not foster a high degree of formal community organization. The Eskimo band was chiefless. Retribution for serious breeches of conduct was usually accomplished by family blood revenge feuding. In some cases, however, regarding major decisions, leadership was assumed by one of the most respected of the band, such as the best hunter or the shaman (Pospisil 1964). Thus, it is clear that much of the Eskimos' cultural life was a functional adaptation to existing on the Arctic coasts via the hunting of the seal, caribou and whale (Birket-Smith 1959).

Most Eskimos today are still acquainted with skin boats; dog sleds; hunting seal, whale, and caribou; certain ceremonial song and dance forms; the large tambourine drum; certain unique aspects of the clothing as the parka, atigi, and mukluk; characteristic artistic styles; the ulu; the oil lamp, etc. On the other hand, each village and each area of Eskimo habitation has its unique social and ecological aspects. In addition, communication to the degree that meaningful social ties are maintained is in most cases limited to the village itself, or as in the case of North Alaska, to adjacent villages (e.g., Pt. Hope, Pt. Lay, Barrow, Wainwright, Kaktovik, and Anaktuvuk Pass). Accordingly, the next section will discuss specific aspects of the Tareumiut and Nunamiut of more recent times.

In summary, this chapter has highlighted the immense antiquity of the Eskimo in North Alaska. Archeological evidences of certain changes in way-of-life through the vast periods of Eskimo occupation in these regions have been described in detail. What is most striking, however, is the relative immutability of the basic features of Eskimo life during the past 5000-6000 years. Tradition has apparently been a most significant and powerful determinant of Eskimo behavior through these ages. His basic industries in hunting caribou and sea mammals have persisted relatively unchanged. Evidences of Kasigies and amulets bear witness to the possible antiquity of the shamanistic practices. Patterns passed on from elder to younger throughout Eskimo history have not profoundly altered. The influences of ancestors of thousands of years ago are still felt by many Eskimos who look to the past for solutions to today's problems.

VI. The Matrix of Eskimo Culture

THE DEVELOPMENT OF A PERSONALITY takes place in a matrix of continuing social experiences and interactions. From the time of his birth and perhaps even before, the child is shaped and molded by the particular cultural milieu within which he is embedded. Constitutional differences in innate response to a given milieu are also undoubtedly important in the formation of personality. However, traditionally, personality development has often been considered in terms of the maturation of the various basic human libidinal strivings, i.e., oral security, anal mastery, and phallic gratification (Freud 1949). More recently, attention has been focused on the growth and development of the adaptive aspects of personality (Hartman 1958; Kris 1952). These models emphasize intrapsychic growth in the formation of personality. They are, of course, not exclusively intrapsychic in orientation. The role of mother and significant stimuli impinging on the developing child from family, school, and other sources is given due consideration.

For the most part, the immense impact on the formation of personality provided by the dynamic web of tradition and custom is not emphasized by these models. A convenient graphic model demonstrating our conception of personality developing and interacting in a dynamic cultural matrix is provided in Figure 3 by a cone representing personality extending in a larger cylinder representing the surrounding matrix of cultural focus.

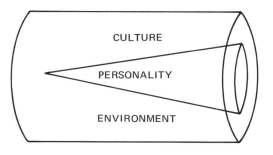

Figure 3.

The cone, like the individual, begins as a point at a point in time. The developing individual gradually expands to occupy more and more of his cultural matrix himself. The configuration of the cone may be distorted along its course from undue external pressure: and at any point in time, a cross section through the cylinder and cone would reveal time-specific, or critical period stimuli and response between these interacting systems. The last chapter extended this basic interactional model into antiquity. The power of the past in determining present-day cultural patterns deepens this perspective (see Figure 4).

This chapter will discuss the recent patterns of North Alaskan Eskimo culture, thus providing the setting from which to understand the development of the individual, who is ultimately afflicted with Arctic Hysteria-like behavior. This discussion will focus on these aspects of the cultural matrix which have had particular influence in shaping the personalities of subjects in this thesis.

Extending from the past

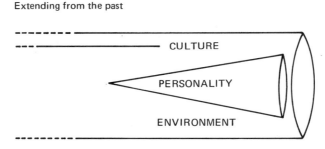

Figure 4.

KINSHIP AND ADOPTION

The North Alaskan Eskimos in no sense constitute a formal tribe. They are considered under one rubric in reference to cultural areas within which are found extensive kinship relations. Aboriginally, the immediate family was the fundamental social unit of the North Alaskan Eskimo. They had no notion of unity as a people, nor were they organized into formal clans. However, they recognized kinship bilaterally through about three generations. Because of their extensive geographical mobility in following game and trading opportunities, there resulted an interwoven pattern of kinship linking most of the North Alaskan villages. Thus in traveling, one could rely on being cared for and fed in a strange village by kinfolk. Without these ties, the traveler would be considered an intruder, and in many cases his reception would be most inhospitable.

Even today, kinship is the basis for expected cooperation in visiting, baby-sitting, fetching ice or coal, checking fish nets, supporting the infirm, etc. In each of these instances, cooperation is implicitly expected; and, if a kinsman does not automatically respond with help to fill an obvious need, he may be the object of much malicious gossip.

One of the few ways kinship privileges and responsibilities could be extended to non-kin was through the ancient Eskimo practice of adoption. Adoption did take place within the extended family; however, there was no consistent pattern to this. Adoptions might occur just as frequently between nonrelated groups. The conditions under which a child was given away usually involved severe economic stress, such as too large a family to feed sufficiently, parental death, or cruel neglect. Milan (1964:62) mentions that seven of forty-one households in Wainwright had eleven adopted children living with them. In three cases, the parents had no children of their own; two of the adopted children were born illegitimately; two had living parents in the village; and the parents of seven others were dead. Many of these adopted children were given names after deceased relatives of the adopting parents, or the same name as someone liked by the adopting parents.

Adopting parents who had previously proven themselves good providers and capable of raising children were preferred. Motivation for adopting was often to extend the kinship circle and thereby enlarge the possibilities for cooperation, in addition to providing insurance for old age when the "children take care of you and look after you" (Spencer 1959:87).

The established pattern of marriage in North Alaska was with parallel or cross-cousins. There is, however, considerable latitude for the young people to choose their own partners now. Marriages take place usually in either a Presbyterian or Assembly of God Church, with the local missionary holding the ceremony. It is strongly encouraged that the young couple establish their own household. However, if they cannot build their own house, they might move back and forth to various in-laws; and, while there are no definite regulations for this, matrilocal residence is seen most often (Milan 1964:62). Spencer (1959:78) maintains that girls were often reluctant to leave the security of their family for a husband, perhaps being unsure of his ability to provide an adequate home. In such cases her parents would often chide her by saying, "Another girl will take him away from you if you don't go to him" or "Look out, some other man will grab you and take you to his house." These remarks not only suggest to the young couple certain expectations of infidelity, but also reflect the Eskimo's general preoccupation with this subject. Jealousy was frequently felt by men and women alike, in spite of such socially acceptable but highly structured practices as wife exchange (Hennigh 1970). For the husband, marital sexual rights were in a sense property rights, and linked with his status as a male. Adultery is actually not uncommon; however, couples involved are subject to much gossip and disrespect.

Premarital sexual experiences, on the other hand, are common and not subject to the same negative social sanctions. Girls are aggressive, if not more so than boys, in their sexual behavior. "Adolescents indulge in considerable erotic play" (Milan 1964:61). The illegitimate child has in the past created little problem, in fact, in many cases enhanced the status of the mother by proving her fertile. Today, however, the more conservative elders and missionaries of the churches feel young people should marry before becoming sexually involved. However, as Chance (1966:50) has pointed out, this attitude is often bypassed, many couples not marrying until after they have children. He regards this pattern as being due to two factors: the economic responsibilities of marriage which are met with difficulty by young men today, and the large degree of sexual freedom available outside of marriage.

Interpersonal relations between husband and wife are in general a reflection of social relations in the larger village society. Rarely are positive feelings or emotions expressed to one another; instead, conversation centers on daily chores or material problems in the household. Positive feelings are often taken for granted to the degree that even gratitude for an extreme service may be unexpressed. Whites are often annoyed by the Eskimo's inability to say "thank you" for services such as medical care, and perceive it as a manifestation of the "dependent welfare personality." Such seeming ingratitude instead probably stems from the Eskimo's traditional expectations of mutual aid and cooperation from all in times of stress. Chance (1966:50) remarks that even when a husband prepares to leave on an extended hunting trip, his wife expresses very little emotion about his departure, nor does she necessarily welcome him home with much gusto, other than to assist him in unloading the meat from the sled. She may, however, communicate some pleasure at his return in nonverbal ways such as smiling and appearing happy.

THE SOCIALIZATION OF THE CHILD

In the past there were many taboos surrounding pregnancy and childbirth; however, today there are no special prescribed behaviors for pregnant women. The fetus is thought of as a "little man" in the body of its mother. Most women in northern villages are flown to the Public Health Service Hospital in Barrow for delivery; however, village midwives are still very active and handle many of the births themselves. A physician who witnessed several of these midwives assisting women in labor, commented that the pulling and tugging which they administer to the baby must frequently result in birth trauma (Milan 1964:57). The child is felt to resemble his father in appearance, as well as temperament. The father of an illegitimate child is, therefore, felt to be easily identified. In the past, infanticide was often practiced in hard times. In some cases where famine prevailed, children were even eaten by the parents (Rasmussen 1931).

Before the child is a month old, he is customarily baptized by the missionary and formally given his name. Today every child receives an English first name, a patrilineal last name, and an Eskimo name which is most personal. The Eskimo name is given to the child by the parents, and is usually a name which was once held by a deceased relative. Some children possess certain personality characteristics reminiscent of a deceased relative and are, therefore, given his name. When a living relative's name is used, he often gives gifts to his namesake, with the belief that after death his spirit will survive in the growing child. This method of bestowing the Eskimo name is in accordance with a belief of the past that humans had both a breath soul and a name soul. The breath soul was immortal and the name soul, only when transferred, carried with it the bodily and mental characteristics of all its previous owners (Milan 1964:60).

Breast feeding was commonly practiced until the child was two to three years old. However, in the last ten years this practice has given way to bottle-formula feeding. The bottle is used to quiet a fussy child long after it is capable of feeding itself. Many children of three or four years can be seen holding bottles to their mouths while playing together out of doors. Verbal expression of emotion, even at this age, is not encouraged, since parents prefer the quiet child and silence the noisy one with placation and stuffing a milk bottle into his mouth. Indeed, at times a most remarkable situation can be observed when, for example, many families gather together at church for Christmas service. Adults sit with heads bowed, praying, while the youngest of children are busy climbing over chairs, running about, and playing with one another in complete verbal silence. All that can be heard is the shuffling and bumping of their feet. If a child begins to cry he is immediately given candy or the bottle to fill his mouth.

Since the daily schedule of eating and sleeping varies considerably throughout the seasons for Eskimo adults, it is not surprising to find that infants rarely have a fixed eating or sleeping schedule. When the baby cries, it is fed. Children are rarely slapped or punished and any expression of aggression toward other children is discouraged. Discipline is rarely imposed on the child until he is actually old enough to get into things; at that point it usually consists of restraining the child.

Children are not expected to be toilet trained until two or three years of age. When young children are being carried about on mother's back beneath her parka, they present some hazard and are thus diapered. Perhaps due to the inefficiency of diapering techniques in past years, an attempt was made to toilet train the child at about age one by holding him over the pot and blowing on his forehead until he excreted (Spencer 1959:235; Chance 1966:21). Today's children, however, are commonly left nude from the waist down. Because of the small, crowded households, whenever the child begins to urinate or defecate, it is usually before a somewhat startled, reacting audience. The child is quickly whisked away to the pot. Such a situation quickly induces a certain sense of "stage fright" which later is expressed with shame and shyness regarding excretory functions. However, Chance (1966:21) remarks that he found no aura of shame or secrecy about excretory functions. This is perhaps partially true among many Innupiat. They seemed all too willing to give details regarding abnormal bowel movements, etc., but this seeming candidness is in many respects rather clinical and impersonal. They are in general not at ease exposing their bodies. Teenage boys, for example, were shy about urinating in each other's presence and would go through considerable inconvenience to avoid doing so (Briggs 1971).

Homes often consist of only one or two rooms, where beds and bunk beds occupy many walls and corners. Children are always close to, if not actually in, the same bed as the parents. They are naturally, therefore, frequent witnesses of parental intercourse no matter how careful the parents might try to be. There is, consequently, much preoccupation with this subject among children. Van Stone (1962:85) mentions two boys who visited him in Pt. Hope, lay on the bed and jokingly imitated the positions of intercourse in playing, despite the fact they were only eight years old. Sex is a constant topic of conversation and jokes among latency age (five to twelve) children, although actual sexual intercourse at this age is uncommon. Adequate privacy for these youths to engage in such practices is difficult to come by, especially during the colder months.

Perhaps because of the large families and crowded houses in most villages, children are encouraged at an early age to play out of doors with siblings or peers. Basketball and tag are favorite games. Older children, however, often feel rather bored wandering around the village, and may pass their time playing cards or secretly smoking with one another in the school doorways. For the most part, many Eskimo children find the enforced containment of the classroom barely tolerable. They are restless; their attention wanders to activities outside the windows; and most seem greatly relieved at the sound of the dismissal bell.

During the past year, many North Alaskan villages have initiated "Head Start" programs for preschoolers, funded by the federal government and staffed by local Eskimo teachers. Before this program, children did not attend school until age five or six. In the village schools which are staffed by young, white, Bureau of Indian Affairs teachers, only English is used. Most preschoolers are unfamiliar with English and, therefore, are at some disadvantage in their early years at school. In general, their achievement is quite low and they are prone to becoming frustrated and apathetic about their academic progress in the first grades. By the eighth grade, however, many youths are sent away from the security of their homes in the village to boarding high schools for American natives, located in various parts of the country. Most go to Mt. Edgecumbe, near Sitka, Alaska, others to Chimawa in Oregon.

While many look forward to this experience as a chance to get out of their small, "boring" village into the hub of "excited," Western living, in most cases they return home disillusioned about their seeming inability to fit into life outside. At the same time, having been away from the village three to four years, they are inept at the skills necessary to be very successful there as well. Milan (1964:61) mentions that these boys who have just returned from years at school are noticeably more attentive to what older hunters tell them, especially when out on the sea ice, and they seem to feel slightly disadvantaged by the time lost in the boarding school. This factor may have contributed much to the demasculinized image that one of our subjects had of himself after returning from not only fours years at Mt. Edgecumbe, but from a year of academic failure at the University of Alaska in Fairbanks, as well. It might be mentioned, however, that attending university is extremely exceptional for these villagers, there having been only two individuals during the past fifteen years having done so, and unsuccessfully at that.

Youths who have returned from high school without skills, or those who for intellectual or other reasons never attended high school, often find themselves included in various government training programs. The story of a young Eskimo man from North Alaska illustrates the stresses such youths may experience. Sam was a man without skills who was chosen by the Fairbanks Office of Economic Opportunities for training in kitchen work at nearby Elison Air Force Base. He was flown from his village and established in a room in a military dormitory outside Fairbanks. He was trained in cleaning floors and paid a fairly substantial salary. Some of it he carefully saved in order to buy a new snow machine for use once he returned to his village. With the remainder of his money, however, he sought to maintain the visiting and social patterns he had formerly been accustomed to at home. During his hours away from mopping floors, he became very lonely and longed for the companionship of friends and relatives. Visiting friends and relatives is in the village a constant activity throughout the day. Being alone, unless on a hunting trip, was rarely experienced. Sam found he did not have the social skills necessary to quickly establish new friendships, since those skills were never learned at home—people there know one another from childhood on. Making "new" friends was a foreign experience. A few Westerns in Fairbanks, however, are willing to provide quick friendship to lonely youths from the villages, especially those who are employed and have a few dollars to spend. White girls from bars in the center of town aggressively made it a point to talk to some of these village boys. Sam interpreted this friendliness as courting behavior, and within a week or so was pining after "his girl, Sally." Sally was employed by the drinking establishment and enjoyed Sam's fifty dollar per bottle California champagne every Saturday night, but obviously had no other more serious designs on him. The situation, in addition to trouble over drunkenness, resulted in final frustration and despair for Sam, who returned to his village after several months somewhat richer in dollars, but not for his experiences.

Eskimo girls from North Alaska seem to acculturate into Western society with perhaps greater ease than the boys, in contrast to the situation reported by Chance (1966) at Barter Island. The female role of housewife in the villages parallels that in Western society, and many young women born in North Alaska now live with white husbands in urban areas of Alaska or the "lower forty-eight" states. Young men, as has been pointed out, seem to find it more difficult assuming the academic or technical skill necessary to making a living outside the village. Thus, young men for the most part return to the village after forays at Westernization; young women do not. This has created an excess of young, eligible bachelors, many of whom aggressively seek female companionship, many times with the married women of the village. This, quite naturally, leads to some trouble and reinforces the jealous attitudes husbands often exhibit toward their wives.

The young men returning to the village who are willing to put forth some effort to learn the Eskimo hunting ways are promptly set against it because of the oftentimes harsh methods of training. Nelson (1969:386-387) aptly summarized the situation of the young man in Wainwright in observing:

Although in former years there was some verbal instruction of youths by older men, there seems to have been a greater emphasis upon practical "on the job" training. This sort of training still persists today. The young hunter accompanies older men on their hunting trips and learns by observing them. If he succeeds in duplicating their actions properly, he is rewarded by silent acceptance. If he should make an error, he is chastised and teased. This ridicule continues beyond that which takes place at the time. The other men are also told of his failings so that they can join in.

The system is very effective, and makes the youth even more determined to succeed under conditions of normal cultural stability. For example, any man who becomes lost or should happen to allow his dog team to run away from him is ridiculed and is considered something of a fool. The fear of such ridicule forces the Eskimo to learn his navigational skills well and to exercise caution whenever he travels. He consciously wishes to escape humiliation due to such errors, and thus, almost unconsciously corrects his mistakes, so that he probably will not face the grave dangers caused by them. Where the stakes are so high, a rigorous training system such as this is extremely effective and adaptive, and assures continuity of the group.

Today, the system is the same, but the response is different. In Wainwright there was only one man in this age group who was willing to learn the skills of hunting. There were many others who did not know these skills and were not willing to undergo the tribulations involved in learning them. This is partially due to the methods of training the physical and psychological difficulties of learning to hunt. The young man must be willing to shrug off continual ridicule and teasing for his errors, and seldom is able to strike a counterblow. The would-be hunters of the past have been required to endure this 'hazing' treatment because for them there was no alternative. Today, however, the youth who returns to the village after completing his formal education is, in the first place, not interested, and must, in addition, face the continual frustration of a learner, if he does attempt to hunt.

SOCIAL CONTROL

Mockery, ridicule, jokes, and gossip are powerful agents of social control among the Innupiat from the bare-bottomed age of two throughout the rest of life. Efficient though these means might be, they serve to render recipients self-conscious, inhibited, and shameful. Some authors (Spencer 1959:238) have pointed out that in the socializaton process the Eskimo stressed cooperation. Competitiveness and showing-off types of behavior were eschewed. It is obvious that with the attitudes which prevail among these people, one must be very sure of himself indeed in venturing to surpass or deviate from the norms of behavior. For even in success, he will be laughed at and considered foolish. Such socialization practices promote the control of individual behavior through shame and fear of "being found out" by others, in contrast to control of individual behavior through internalized guilt and a sense of doing wrong whether others "find out" or not.

In addition to these informal methods of enforcing social sanctions, several institutionalized methods of explicity setting rules and enforcing them exist in many villages today. First among these is the village council. The original organization of the village councils followed the Indian Reorganization Act, Section 16, of June 18, 1934 (Milan 1964:53), wherein the Eskimo obtained the right to draw up a village constitution and laws and ratify them by majority vote. The councils are organized formally with an elected president, vice-president, secretary, treasurer, and councilmen. They usually meet monthly and deal with such problems as the operation of the Native Cooperative Store, mediation with the goals of the white BIA schoolteachers, and enforcement of local regulations. Law enforcement, however, is in most cases not directly punitive. Offenders are usually simply asked to stop. If illegal behavior continues, the matter is brought before the council, who in turn asks the offender to publicly account for his behavior. It would appear that mere public confession of rule violations before mutely disapproving neighbors in the council in most cases serves the purpose of controlling deviant behavior. Aboriginally, these Eskimos lacked formal government; however, they did possess numerous taboos concerning methods of eating, intercourse, songs, amulets, etc. Community disasters were attributed by the shaman to certain individuals having violated one of the many taboos. Commonly, the solution to the disaster in the community was to allow the offending individuals to confess publicly. In essence, certain individuals were scapegoated, so that the community could rationalize the disaster which had befallen it, at the same time reinforcing social controls. Eisenmann (1965) pointed out that the Eskimo offender was more often viewed as "one who simply forgot the rules" like a wayward child, and so felt little hesitation in confessing his transgressions. If an offender's behavior was so deviant, however, as to seriously disrupt the society, he may have been ostracized or murdered in the past.

The most frequently occurring problems presented to the councils involve illicit sexual behavior, drinking, and curfew violations. Milan (1964:54) observed the following list of rules posted on the wall of the native store:

1. No intoxicating beverages allowed in this village.
2. No gambling with dice or cards.
3. The placing of lighted matches in empty gas drums for the pleasure of the explosion is forbidden.
4. Forbidden to damage windows of buildings or other peoples' houses. The person damaging will be liable to fine and to pay damages.
5. Obey the laws of the United States.

Many of the negative sanctions laid down by the village councils are alternately derived from attitudes generated by the churches in the villages. Indeed, among the most powerful agents of formal social control are the Presbyterian and Assembly of God preachers and elders. The original church in North Alaska was Presbyterian, under an agreement by the Federal Council of Churches in the 1890s, which divided the region into several missionary regions (Jenness 1962:10); Barrow, Wainwright, and Anaktuvuk Pass were assigned to the Presbyterians, and Pt. Hope and Pt. Lay to the Episcopalians. Early missionaries in the area were mocked and the objects of much ridicule (Spencer 1959:380). However, the church caught on rather quickly. The reason for this unquestionably is partly due to the ease with which Christian doctrine blended into aboriginal beliefs. Eskimos always were somewhat anxious about having shaman in their village, and, to a certain extent, welcomed the Christian missionary's antagonism to him. Appropriately, they identified the Eskimo shaman's *tunraq*, or demonic spirit, as the Devil of Christian belief. Alignuk, the Moon Man, the incestuous brother of Sugunnug, the Sun, became identified with the Christian God. As mentioned previously, the Eskimos also had beliefs in human souls, one immortal, the other the name soul, which corresponded compatibly with Christian belief (Milan 1964:67). Singing and sociability, offered through the medium of church meetings, has also enchanced the conversion of the Eskimos. The aboriginal concept of taboo violation was quickly identified with the Christian concept of sin. However, committing sins seldom resulted in guilt and inner self-condemnation; instead, the offender expected communal or personal disaster to befall him. Illness was, and still is, commonly seen in this respect. Missionaries often complain that parishioners often seem to lack much depth of feeling in their frequent public testimonials and confessions. Self-castigation and resolutions for future good behavior are proclaimed, yet the motive for such confession seems to be more of a public announcement of misdeeds, rather than a personal expression of repentance. It would appear that the attitude during confession in church is much the same as the attitude of confession before the village council.

Recently, a more fundamentalistic church, the Assembly of God, has stationed missionaries in North Alaska. Most people have continued their affiliation with the established Presbyterian Church. However, the Assembly of God has attracted many new converts. In part, this may be due to the service being more congregation-oriented. In the Presbyterian Church, the greater part of the service is devoted to the minister's preaching a sermon consisting of a rather abstract message from the Bible. The Assembly of God, on the other hand, allows for frequent public testimonial of faith, and confessions from the congregation. In addition, this church believes in curing illness through the "laying on of hands" and confession of sins, as well as "speaking in tongues" through the presence of the Holy Spirit. These practices are both clearly parallel to aboriginal concepts of the causes and cures of illness and of spirit possession.

An elderly man of the church gave the following testimonial one evening:

One night I camp on the Tundra looking to hunt caribou. Suddenly my bones ache all over; I was weak and laid on the floor; couldn't move; I was alone and thought I would die. Then I wake up and saw a little, white Jesus standing in the doorway of the tent. He said to me, get up, you'll be alright. I got up and felt strong all over. Oh, thank you, Jesus!

BELIEFS FROM THE PAST

North Alaskan Eskimos still halfheartedly believe in the existence of "little men." These creatures are said to be about one foot tall and live in the tundra in the same manner as Eskimos. Despite their small size, they are said to be very powerful and can in most cases defeat humans in combat. Their tracks have often been seen and they always disappear or lead to the ocean. "Little men" are often heard singing or making noises like the wolf. Spencer (1959:261) mentions that in 1952 a fire was sighted some distance down the beach from Wainwright. Everyone in the village was accounted for, hence explaining the fire was difficult. The general consensus was that "little men" were camping on the beach, and it was their campfire which was sighted. The presence of natural gas and oil near the surface of the area was at that time unknown to the people of that area. One of Milan's informants, Taqalaq, told of mortal combat between his grandfather and a "little man" that supposedly took place many years ago after his grandfather won a foot race around the shore of an inland lake (Milan 1964:69). Parents can be heard frequently admonishing their naughty children with threats that "the little people will get you if you're not good." Another frequent threat to children if they misbehave is, "the 'tunniks' (white man) will get you." The old man's "little white Jesus," benevolent as he was, reflects a transfiguration of aboriginal foes into Christian friend.

The *tunraq*, one of the demonic spirits (Marsh 1954:27) has been mentioned inasmuch as with the advent of Christianity he became equated with the emissaries of Satan. Before this it was believed that *tunraq* would often randomly take his abode in anyone; however, it was felt that he must be resisted at any cost lest he "take your life and give you the shaman's life." Ordinary persons depended primarily on amulets and individual charms, but it was believed that with caution they could at times employ other spirits as well. The difference between ordinary persons and the shaman was for the most part quantitative rather than qualitative. Shamans were individuals who had more skill at dealing with the supernatural than did ordinary people, thus being able to control more spirit power and still live. Chief among these powers were the *tunraq*, demonic spirits who emanated from the souls of certain land animals, namely brown bear, wolf and fox, and rarely from the souls of "little men."

The Shaman

People did not voluntarily seek to become shamans. In some cases, an old shaman would recognize certain personality qualities in a youth, which would indicate that he was a good candidate for tutelage. Not infrequently, a youth traveling alone on the tundra would hear his name being called by a *tunraq*. If he answered the call, the power of the *tunraq* would be his; however, he would be doomed from that moment on to the fears and turmoils of dealing with the supernatural. While virtually anyone could become a shaman through such experiences, in practice the role was often passed from father to son, or from a man to another close relative. Shamanistic power seemed to run in certain families (Gubser 1965:156; Spencer 1959:303). On the other hand, Rasmussen (1938) observed among the Angmagssalik Eskimos that orphans were often the chosen subjects for shamanism.

Transvestism and homosexuality have been reported as common characteristics of the shamans (Bogoras 1904-1909:455). Murphy (1964:75) mentions that on St. Lawrence Island the term for an effeminate man was *anasik*, and there reportedly were five men living together at one time who looked like women and who dressed like women. None of them hunted; instead they were provided for by neighbors. They were said to be "good singers" which was felt by the author to be an oblique reference to the fact that they may have been shamans.

For the most part, the daily life of a shaman was no different than anyone else's. No special status was accorded him because of his spirit power. If anything, people felt uneasy about having him around because of the potential malevolence he could muster. Most people felt that a young man could not assume the role of shaman adequately, even though he may have demonstrated his powers on occasion. Tutelage involved the learning of certain songs, ventriloquism, "speaking in tongues" of animals, and many magical tricks, such as vomiting up objects, tying knots in strings held in the mouth, making objects appear and disappear, driving knives into the flesh without bleeding, etc.

Shamans became most active in holding seances to demonstrate their power during the dark winter months of November, December, and January. Today the month of November in Eskimo is called Uvluilaq Taatqiq, the moon of short days. In the past this period was known as Kiyeevilwik, the time when the shamans get busy (Spencer 1959:304). The shaman would summon the community when illness, food shortage, bad weather, or other mishaps occurred. Often the meeting would result in a seance which commenced with the shaman beating his drum and chanting his own powerful songs in an intense rhythmic fashion. With the darkness, the heat and stuffiness of the crowded situation in the house, and the rising tempo of drumming and chanting, the group would often become spellbound and somewhat fearfully in awe of what was to happen. At such a point, the shaman often stopped his frenzied beats and lapsed into trance-like silence. Voices of spirits would be heard at this time calling from doorways and the roof, often in the tones of his *tunraq*, a wolf or bear growl. Such a trance might continue for many hours. When the shaman was seen to move again, it was thought that his soul was returning. Often the performances became extremely frenzied, with the shaman wildly dancing about, his eyes rolling back, his clothes ripped off and his body sweating profusely. Intimidated audiences agreed, "he was a devil," "he acted like crazy" (Spencer 1959:307).

Today, people in North Alaska profess to be Christians and generally will say little about shamans. As late as the mid 1950s, however, it was said that there was an old woman at Wainwright who practiced shamanism (Spencer 1959:381). Milan's informant, Iqaaq, told him about a *tunraq* of a dead shaman who lived near the village of Atanik, who would cry out when people went past during the winter. He was felt to be dangerous. He also told of a large stone at Tutulivik, three miles from Wainwright, that once had been a shaman. People would bring offerings of meat and blubber to gain good luck in hunting (Milan 1964:69). It is well known that many people have had considerable experience with shamans in the recent past. Spencer (1959:318-323) cited the following episodes:

There was a man who was not a shaman although he knew many songs associated with shamanism. When still a young man, he had lived at Wainwright and was in contact with a powerful shaman there. This Angatquq (shaman) said, "I'm going to take your life and give you the life of the Angatquq." He made him sit down by him in the house. The shaman put his head between his knees and went into a trance. The young man felt the influence working on him. He began to fall forward and felt his eyes turning inward. But he grabbed at his ankles and kept himself from "going out" . . . The shaman said, "Now you are going out for the winter hunting. You will take eight wolves. When you have taken that many, come back to me and I will take away your life and give you the Angatquq's life" . . . When he had seven wolves, he became frightened and tried to avoid taking another. He turned back and drove toward the settlement. Suddenly his dogs stopped. Sticking up in the snow, he saw an ear. He dug around it and found the eighth wolf. He realized the shaman's prophecy was fulfilled. But when he got back, the shaman had died and the young man did not have to become a shaman.

. . . Once when the informant and his family were camped for the winter, there came another man and stayed with them awhile. He began to get more and more nervous. Finally he said, "Get me a flint blade, as wide as your hand and twice as long." They gave him one of these. As he took it, he became tense and his eyes rolled. He took off his parka and shirt and sat naked in the house. He began to talk to himself. Suddenly he plunged the blade into his chest and worked it into his breast bone. Blood spurted out from between his fingers. He pushed the whole blade into the breast bone, working it in gradually until it disappeared. He fell forward as if dead, remaining in a trance-like state for some time. At last he came to his senses, got up and left the house. It was noted that he had a red mark on his chest, but there was no wound. . .

There was a shaman at Wainwright named Kovanna. He married a woman with a daughter by a previous marriage. When they had been married for sometime, the daughter, Ayranna, became ill and was close to death. Her mother told her stepfather, the shaman, that if he could cure her, he might take her as his wife. He succeeded in curing her, and, although he made no demand on her at the time, let it be understood that she was to become his wife. At a later time the girl's mother separated from Kovanna and went with her daughter to Barrow. After they had been there for some time, the mother died. The shaman, Kovanna, then came from Wainwright to claim Ayranna. She was afraid of him at first because of his power, but he overcame her fears and succeeded in marrying her. It was agreed that this was right, that the shaman in effect was taking his fee.

There was a man who lived near Wainwright up the coast and a little inland from the town. When winter came, he and his family didn't have enough food. They even ate their dogs. Then the man decided to go to Wainwright and get food. He took a sled and dragged it behind him; he was very weak. After awhile, he lost his way in the dark. He camped near some old abandoned houses, but was afraid to go into them. He built a snow house and slept there. While he was asleep, he heard his name being called. In his half-sleep, he answered, "yes". Then he awoke and was alone. He was horribly afraid and went on to Wainwright. He sat all trembling . . . and related what had happened to him. "Something is now touching me, it has its hands on my back . . . something has stuck its finger up my rectum," he cried. He went to the fire and picked up the burning ashes in his hands, pouring them into his parka by the handfuls. He dropped his trousers and rubbed kerosene into his anus. "They still touch me," he yelled . . . After a moment he said, "There is my father-in-law's face looking down at me; he is looking in, he is looking in." The man's father-in-law had been a great shaman. He turned away from the skylight so that the face couldn't look at him, but it appeared on the other side of the room, still looking at him. He screamed, "Aw, aw" and fell into a faint. After that, he couldn't do anything. He just sat around and wouldn't talk and wouldn't answer when people talked to him. He just sat staring. But every once in awhile he said things were touching him. In the Spring he was sent out from Wainwright to the A.N.S. doctors. They took him to Morningside (Oregon Mental Hospital) and he stayed there 2 years. At last they sent him back on the North Star. For awhile he was alright. But one day he was carrying a large piece of driftwood and something grabbed it from behind and he couldn't go on. After that, he couldn't work anymore and he said things were touching him. They sent him to the hospital again and he died there.

Much debate has occurred among anthropologists regarding the psychological functioning of the shaman. One position holds that the shaman is a sham, a theatrical faker, who has simply learned a complex repertoire of tricks in fulfilling a necessary role in society (Ackerknecht 1943:46). The other point of view is that most shamans are highly disturbed individuals who experience delusions, hallucinations, and disturbances of affect typical of the hysteric or schizophrenic (Laubscher 1937). Any such generalizations about shamans, however, are certain to be fraught with as many inconsistencies and contradictions as trying to characterize the "typical leader" or the "typical criminal." Shamanism, however, does provide a convenient role for some individuals who are otherwise disturbed. In addition, the practices and beliefs of the shaman posed a model of behavior for others to potentially utilize in times of personal distress. Dissociating one's anxious mind into the realm of the supernatural is a familiar human mechanism for handling problems unsolvable by other means. Kroeber pointed out how this mechanism is merely a shift in emphasis of normal psychic life. The primitive may "not really fail to discriminate the objective from the subjective, the normally natural from the supernatural. He distinguishes them much as we do. He merely weights or favors the supernatural, as we disfavor and try to exclude it. The voice of the dead, the dream, and the magic act stand out for him from the run of commonplace experience of reality much as they do for us; but he endows them with a quality of special superreality and desirability, we of unreality and undesirability. The values have changed, rather than the perception. And values are cultural facts" (Kroeber 1952:313).

Several recent investigations have been conducted on the personality of the Alaskan Eskimo shamans. Margaret Lantis (1960) obtained autobiographical accounts and administered Rorschach cards to two shamans on Nunivak Island. The first shaman had a physically deformed leg, and it was felt that he attempted to use magical power as a defensive overcompensation to overcome this deficiency and his antagonism with his father. He had gone into fantasy life soon after a period of great personal anxiety. Despite ambivalence toward his father, this shaman admired his power and knowledge of the supernatural and identified with him. His Rorschach protocol was rated by two independent psychologists, neither having knowledge of Eskimo culture or the identity of the individuals. Their findings of this shaman are as follows (Lantis 1960:182-183):

Introversion-extroversion: More extroverted, some blocking or both
Affection: Moderate
Sex Conflict: High (some of the myths . . . clearly contain sex symbolism, with indications of homosexuality)

Anxiety: High
Sources of Anxiety: Relations with people and own incompetence
Feelings of Guilt: None or slight, at least for conscious guilt
Conformity-individuality: Little individuality
Adjustment: Poor
Sense of Adjustment Problems: Difficulties with other people . . .physical competence
Energy: Moderate or slight
Persistence: Moderate or slight
Pathology: No; possibly
Nature of Pathological Trends or Symptoms: Suspicion. One rater added that perhaps the
    subject was hysteric: impulsive and had homosexual tendencies or was impotent
Aggressiveness and Inhibition of Aggressive Impulses: Aggression high, with moderate inhibition
Intelligence: High average; low average

Lantis also described a female shaman who during a critical period in her youth lost her mother
and turned to the spirit world for comfort. There came a point in her experience with the spirits at
which she lost all fear of them, and in fact undoubtedly enjoyed them. This woman had
experienced considerable rejection by her real father, her mother deserted her, her foster mother
was inadequate, and her older sister disliked her. In addition, she had much guilt in terms of
Eskimo culture and in terms of the new culture.

According to old culture, she was guilty because she and her sister were quarrelsome and
aggressive and because she, like all shamans having strong spirit-powers, was charged with
witchcraft. In the new culture she was guilty of sexual offense and of the mere practice of
shamanism . . . she had acquired the powers in the first place in order to fight a
community that must have seemed hostile to her [Lantis 1960:137-138].

Rorschach analysis of this woman shaman revealed:

Subject has little or no sex conflict . . .
Is highly aggressive . . . to men . . . possibly others.
Subject's principal defense is suppression . . . projection and escape into activity . . . repression,
    avoidance and evasion.
Has slight or no dependency strivings.
Has marked wish to dominate.
Is highly competitive.
Is very jealous.
Is concerned with achieving security in interpersonal relations (emphasis is on the concern, the
    anxiety, rather than achievement).
Source of her adjustment problems is "people" rather than "internal conflicts" in physical
    competence.
Has no "need achievement."
Is neither especially flexible nor rigid.
Has no pathology; but (one rater) added, "some suspicion of paranoid trends . . . possibility of
    hysterical symptoms or some somatic involvement not excluded."
Adjustment not good.
. . . There appears a picture of a woman who wants to get along with people, but who, because
    of need to dominate, competitiveness, suspicion and jealousy, cannot do so and has
    anxieties, both conscious and unconscious . . .
Hers was an essentially tragic life, somewhat relieved by her shamanism, subjectively by the
    escape from reality that it provided, objectively by its accomplishments for community good
    [Lantis 1960:183-185].

Despite the fragmentary nature of the data on these two shamans, it is evident that their
psychologies are by no means the same. Their calls to shamanism were based on two different
personal dynamics; the first defended against his physical inadequacies, the second sought status
and expiation of her guilt.

On St. Lawrence Island, Murphy (1964:69) observed that the Eskimos did not themselves
consider shamans insane—shamans were thought to be "out of mind" but not crazy. These
possession states were more the mark of curing abilities rather than of mental disease itself.
Between 1940 and 1955, eighteen shamans were identified practicing in a population of 250.
Psychiatric symptoms displayed by these individuals were no greater or less than the population as
a whole (Murphy 1964:76). The most powerful shamans were, if anything, very well balanced
mentally. She concludes, however, that the role of shaman did provide an available opportunity

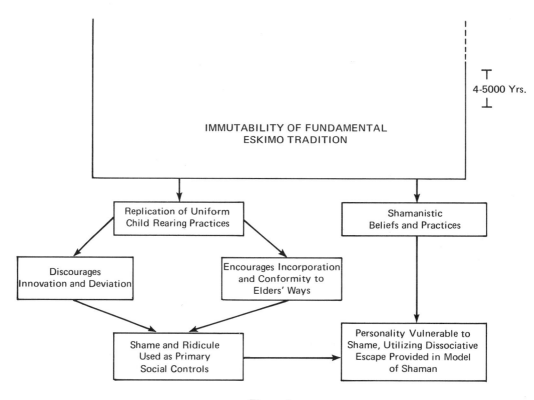

Figure 5.

for anyone who was mentally disturbed to find an acceptable niche in his society.

Spencer (1959:301) felt that the aboriginal cultures of North Alaska called forth behaviors of a neurotic, hysterical, or psychotic nature, created circumstances which induced them, and rewarded them when they appeared. "The imperfectly understood phenomenon of the so-called 'Arctic Hysteria', whatever its environmental or cultural causes, is unquestionably a factor in shamanism and in the molding of the would-be shamanistic practitioner." Earlier Ohlmarks (1939) had concluded that "the original home of shamanism was the arctic, and its original source was 'Arctic Hysteria'."

Eskimos have inhabited Arctic Alaska for many thousands of years. During this long period their way of life has changed very little. Until the present era, those changes that did come about usually occurred over many generations. Thus differences between our generation and the next were usually not experienced by the Eskimo. The growing child was encouraged to emulate the roles and life style lived by his grandparents and the other old people of the group. A youth gained pride and status if he could attain feats accomplished by some legendary ancestor who lived hundreds of years before him. Children were born and old people died; generation followed generation, but the Eskimo way of life continued relatively unaltered. For the growing child there were no psychological alternatives to the prescribed, traditional roles he would be expected to fill as he grew older. Life was mapped out, structured, and predetermined according to the patterns which had been time tested for hundreds of generations. In Eskimo society, he always knew his place and was certain of his roles. These prescribed structures and many ways for life offered a security and acceptance, but in some ways resulted in psychological burdens. Deviance from the normal daily rounds of behavior whether it take the form of innovation, leadership, or expression of hostility was not tolerated by the group. Gross deviance often threatened the group to the point of ostracizing or murdering the offender. Minor or accidental transgressions were usually joked about or ridiculed. Interpersonal conflicts were occasionally resolved by traditional means such as the song contests or shamanistic seances.

The traditional Eskimo way of life was highly specialized and adaptive to living in the Arctic. Deviance from these time tested ways perhaps realistically endangered a group's survival. Adherence to these ways ensured food, shelter, and cooperative relations with others most of the time. No society, however, is able to meet all the needs, or solve all the conflicts of its members. In groups perhaps less dependent on traditional methods than the Eskimo, these unmet needs and unresolved conflicts might be satisfied through channels of personal expression and innovation. In Eskimo society, personal expression outside the prescribed channels was usually met with ridicule and joking. Eskimos, however, did recognize "soul trips" or mental dissociations as legitimate behaviors which did solve many practical and personal problems through magical beliefs. These soul trips were recognized as being beyond the personal control and responsibility of the individual. The prototype for this dissociative behavior was present throughout the life of the growing Eskimo child in the personage of the shaman. Every Eskimo was a bit of a shaman, some only more than others.

Hardships and dissatisfactions of life are accepted "fatalistically" by the Eskimo because from his perceptual standpoint his life could not possibly be any different than it is. He is fatalistic because from early youth he has few choices in determining his own life and fate. Dissatisfactions and conflicts in living are accepted as part of being an Eskimo man, or Eskimo woman. Powerless in resolving these conflicts, the Eskimo has expressed his frustrations in the frenzy of his shamanizing with Arctic Hysteria-like behavior. Figure 5 summarizes the interrelationships of these social forces.

VII. The Arctic Hysterias of the Alaskan Innuit 1969-70

THE PRESENT-DAY LIFE of the North Alaskan Eskimo is changing rapidly. These changes have resulted from a complex series of recent historical events. The traditional, small Eskimo group was highly adapted to a hunting economy. The small group size allowed for efficient harvesting of caribou and sea mammals within a range determined by the nomadic and migratory abilities of the group. A given area of the Arctic can sustain only a certain number of animals, which of course determines the quantity of meat available to an Eskimo group. In most cases these food sources permitted populations of a very limited size. Often population size was maintained at low numbers by practices of infanticide and suicide, as well as high infant mortality from birth trauma and infectious disease. These small groups adhered to traditional, time tested ways of hunting and living their daily lives. Joking, mocking, and ridiculing were used in shaping and socializing the individual. Shamanism was practiced and provided a model for the occasional release of conflict. The Arctic Hysterias were also manifest under similar circumstances.

With the coming of Western government and Christian values, this situation was changed. The North Alaskan Eskimo settled into permanent communities to be near church and school. This decreased the efficiency of his hunting. In addition, Christian values did not permit infanticide or suicide, and population expanded. Medical care has further reduced neonatal and infant mortality, which also increased the population despite tragic reductions during the epidemics of measles and tuberculosis. Soon the Eskimo community became too large for an exclusive hunting economy. In the meantime, Western cash economy was introduced, and many families were given social security benefits. Maintaining strict adherence to traditional ways was no longer adaptive. In addition, shamanisn was equated with Satan, and forbidden. The Arctic Hysterias correspondingly have become a rare event in North Alaska. There were several such Innuit, however, who were brought to my attention during field studies in North Alaska in 1969-70.

As consulting psychiatrist for the Northern Regional Clinic, Division of Mental Health located in Fairbanks, I was responsible for administering psychiatric care to any individual living north of a line drawn from Fairbanks to Nome. The population included almost all Innuit Eskimos living in Alaska. Also included were Athabascan Indians and whites who were also settled in the northern regions. The position enabled me to review directly cases of mental disorders which occurred among the Innuit from July 1969 through June 1970. Cases were often initially referred from the village health aide who was Eskimo, or from the local school teacher, public health worker, or minister. During this time, there were ten individuals who had manifested behavior similar in pattern to the Arctic Hysterias. All of them had actually been diagnosed as such before I had seen them. A number of these cases came from villages remote from the central focus of my fieldwork. Therefore, clinical description of these cases was necessarily more limited.

CASE #1 — AMOS

This is the life of Amos, an Innuit in his mid-twenties, who has experienced periodic "spells" since the time of his puberty. Amos' mother was not married at the time of his birth. She had had two previous children, the eldest a boy and the second child a girl, four years older than Amos. When Amos was three weeks old, his mother abandoned the three children and went to live in another town. The three children were immediately adopted by a kindly, childless couple. Villagers remarked that the adopting parents were too indulgent and "spoiled" the children by giving in to their every wish. One of the old midwives who was present at Amos' birth remembers that while Amos' mother was in the last three months of her pregnancy, she was "behaving very strangely; she would stare into space." After his birth, however, she was again quite normal. There was no other history on his mother's side of disturbed behavior or supernatural experiences. The situation on his father's side, however, was quite different.

Many of the older people of the village still remember Amos' paternal grandfather. They still speak about "his great power; sometimes he went and acted real crazy; he always talked to the spirits; sometimes he got real wild and would beat his family." Amos' father was said "not to be as powerful as the grandfather, but he was real crazy too. He was real jealous, he'd run after people and fly into a fury; sometimes he'd stay out on the tundra by himself long time." Amos' father also left the village shortly after his son was born. Many people in the city where he eventually settled remember this man and his frequent attacks of "fury." During these times he was said to be fantastically destructive, breaking windows, smashing furniture, at times running out into the street screaming. He was jailed and hospitalized a number of times. Amos never knew either one of his parents personally. He had never met them, although he knew he was adopted and had heard stories about his grandfather and his father's behavior.

Amos' adoptive father was a kind gentleman, who took great interest in his adopted children. He was a religious man of the Presbyterian faith and every night before bed would read a portion of the scripture to the children before they went to sleep. Amos was always a serious youth, very interested in religion; and, for this reason, was said to be his adoptive father's favorite child. Most significant during the period of Amos' latency was the fact that he shared a room with a very old granduncle who had been infirm and confined to bed for many years. Amos would spend hours with this old man, "That man taught me a lot about old-fashioned ways; he told me where power comes from; he told me how to get it; then he died." Amos states that shortly after the death of this old man, supernatural things began to happen to him:

> Things that I can't explain, that nobody really believes. When I was ten years old my father told me to fill a can with gasoline. I went out and looked at the gasoline drum; it was big; it was too heavy; I couldn't budge it. I knew my father wanted me to do that, so I got down on my hands and knees and prayed to God. Suddenly a spirit entered my body and I felt strong all over; it was a miracle; I could pick up the whole drum over my head [he demonstrated with his arms]; and I was only a boy. Ever since that time supernatural things happen to me; when I'm alone, out on the tundra, hunting for caribou, sometimes my mind leaves me, I become strong; this has happened two or three times a year, since I've been ten years old.

As a youth, Amos had severe otitis media. Pus drained chronically from both ears; however, in adulthood the condition subsided. When he was twelve or thirteen years old he was hit on the head by a chunk of ice and knocked unconscious. He went to school to the eighth grade and was then separated from his family and sent to a boarding school to continue his education. While there he experienced, "communications in my mind, which tell me to go to preach the Scriptures to all the people. The communications told me where to go and where to preach; it was like a voice, but it was in my mind."

While a student at the boarding school he experienced a severe fall from a bicycle. A witness mentioned that he thought he had a seizure when he fell and that he was "crazy like and real sick" after he fell. He returned to the village and resumed hunting caribou, seal and whale, and trapping. One day in 1966, Amos was on a boat trip with a number of other men. While at sea in a skin boat (umiak) Amos "became unmanageable, throwing his arms and legs around and frothing at the mouth." The crew members restrained him and started to take him back to the village. After a while Amos started feeling better and persuaded the men to continue the trip. Amos had no memory whatsoever for this episode.

Amos had heard so much about his father that during the summer of 1967 he decided to go to the city and find him. When he arrived he was told that several weeks previously his father had gone into a rage, and had been throwing furniture around his small home. Something had happened to ignite a fire and his father had burned to death and the house had burned down. Amos returned immediately to the village; there he became even more engrossed in the Presbyterian Church. He developed a very close attachment to an Eskimo man who was an ordained minister of the Church. He was around the Church constantly. During this time Amos also became enamored of a young woman named Lilly. She was a very immature woman, afraid to go outside, preferring to be with her parents constantly. Amos and Lilly became very close to one another, and developed an intense dependency that mutual jealousy was a constant issue even if one of them casually glanced or conversed with another person. They slept together and Lilly became pregnant.

After an illness, the Eskimo minister died. Amos did not grieve, however, instead one evening when discussing hunting with his wife and her family he made some veiled comments about what it would be like to freeze on the tundra. The family did not take him seriously, as he had always been a good hunter and knew his way around. As it is dark most of the time during that period of the year, villagers do not remember just what time of day he set out. Several hours later, however, his dog team returned to the village with an empty sled. They thought little of it, as it was common to have dog teams get away and return home on their own. But, after he did not return to the village within several hours, search parties were organized. He was finally found in the dark walking away from the lights of the village. He seemed to be in a daze; they had difficulty in convincing him to return home. He remarked that "I was called by God." He felt called by God, and since the Eskimo minister died, he felt that it was he who should be the spiritual leader of his people. In June his daughter was born. People say that Amos was in a disgruntled mood most of the day. Apparently his mother-in-law early one morning insisted that he cut ice so that it could be melted for water. He did not respond, so she began to nag him to get busy and make jokes about his masculinity. Finally, he went to his adoptive father to borrow the snowmobile; he said "these Pentacostal people are so bossy." Several hours later he returned with the river ice. He was obviously quite agitated. After unloading the ice he entered the house and with a scream grabbed his throat with both hands and tried to strangle himself. After being stopped, he dashed out of the house and went to his adoptive parents' home. He returned that evening apparently in his full senses. He stated that he remembered what happened quite well and goes on to tell:

> About 12:00 a.m. I was lying in bed with my wife and had a vision. I don't know whether anyone can understand this, but here's the way it went. I walking through a town that looked a lot like our village, there was a church and a graveyard nearby. All the people in town were out drunk, drinking whiskey and fighting with each other and doing all kinds of things and I was watching this; and there were also some people running around on top of the graves who came from the town. Then I saw other people coming up from the graves, rising from the dead; this was a vision. I saw them drinking and fighting. At first I didn't feel anything at all; I felt like I was right there, but I wasn't doing what they were doing. I had no feeling about it at all. Then I felt that all these people were evil.

He got out of bed and began to ask others in the household why they did not get up. By this time it was 12:00 a.m. He ran to his adoptive father's house and asked them to get up. His father thought that he was acting like he was drunk; but he could smell no liquor on his breath. Amos began praying and rocking; he then got up and began to beat his wife and his father on the head. His brother-in-law came in, and the family was able to restrain him. They said, "He had foam in his mouth." They held him until 7:00 in the morning when he finally went to sleep. While he slept people sat with him and watched him. They took turns until the next day. At about one o'clock the village health aide attempted to arouse him. He responded only with nods or shakes of his head. About five minutes later he suddenly "came to" fighting, and had a seizure with lots of foaming and saliva coming out of his mouth. After being subdued he went back to sleep.

He spent the following five months at the Alaska Psychiatric Institute. During that time staff noted that he had "spells" on three occasions. Apparently, when he became annoyed or angry "he would suddenly fall backwards on to the bed or floor. His body would become rigid, with his arms outstretched and he was biting as hard as he could. There was no loss of consciousness or incontinence; the were no clonic convulsive movements. During one of these spells he was given intravenous valium (a tranquilizer). He believed it to be truth serum and soon began to talk about how he beat his wife "because she really loves others and not me." He was returned to the village in December. At that time he was described by villagers as being extremely "docile." He had been away from his wife and child and family. It was noted that after his return from the hospital "he no longer acted like a man." He never again went out hunting or trapping, but preferred to stay at home or walk about the village. He was cajoled and nagged constantly to act "like a man." He was always friendly and communicative, but seemingly had lost all confidence in himself to act independently. He became even more dependent upon his wife and his mother-in-law, and moved his things into his mother-in-law's house. He openly expressed his desire to be taken care of by his mother-in-law. She and a number of other people in the village began to jest and make fun of him, making jokes about "Amos is now a woman; he acts like a woman." Then he said, "I am going to get a place of my own; I'm going to take my wife and baby to live in my own house; there's a place I know that's going to be empty soon; maybe I can rent it. I'm going to get a job and make money and then become a minister." Soon afterward one night Amos was seen coming out of his room carrying an ulu (an Eskimo knife). He appeared dazed and would not respond to his father's inquiries. He walked "like a zombie" out the door, heading for his mother-in-law's house. His father grabbed him and called for help. A number of men were aroused and came to his aid. All said that Amos "had the strength of ten men; he had supernatural strength." When he awoke he said, "My wife doesn't want me any more; she wants someone else; I know she loves someone else. I don't know who it is. Everyone in the village hates me. They all want to get rid of me; no one wants me." For several days Amos had episodes of sitting up in bed with a fixed stare on his face, or rocking back and forth on his hands and knees. He was unable to communicate during these episodes. While in this state he would often tie his pajama tops around his neck and pull them tight. This would usually result in some rapid breathing and a red face on his part. He was not restrained during any of these spells and they would characteristically last only thirty to forty-five minutes.

Soon, in addition to his mother-in-law's calling him a "woman," many of the villagers would mock him in his presence. They would discuss lurid details of what Amos looked like during his convulsions. Amos isolated himself more and more from village life. Many people began to make obtuse statements along the lines of "maybe next time you go out into the tundra alone, we won't find you." He was psychologically ostracized; no one would have much to do with him. However, they did talk to Lilly. He was torn between leaving the security of the village of his boyhood where he was now obviously unwanted, or staying and enduring the mocking and derision of family and village members. His wife and her mother joined in, and berated Amos for having the "thoughts of a woman." He expressed to me as each day went by an increasing shame about his wife, his mother-in-law, and other people in the village talking about him behind his back, talking about the fact that he is no longer a hunter and that he has "the thoughts of a woman." He finally separated from his wife and child and his mother-in-law and went to live with his adoptive father. He remained alone in his room most of the time and did not bother to communicate with others. Several weeks later, he took an ice pick and carved two long lacerations down the palmer surface of his left forearm. He bled profusely, but he called for no help. Instead, several days later he showed me his arm and said that "It was sort of a suicide attempt; God has required that I suffer in this world." He again retreated into his room and became uncommunicative. One month later, just before Christmas, he left a note with his father, addressed to his wife. It read, "I am going for a long, long walk." Following this, he went down to the beach winter trail, heading for another village about one hundred miles distant. He was found about an hour later, heading back toward the village along the well-traveled winter path. When he returned to the village he was noticeably agitated. He exhibited gross tremor of both hands and he stammered a great deal during conversation. He told me that he had been bothered a long time by thoughts that while he was away from his house his wife was spending time with her alleged boyfriend. He had no one in particular in mind to accuse of consorting with his wife, but said that they must be "teenagers. Even they are more manly then me." He said:

> Since Lilly and I been married we never been alone; we've always lived with her mother or my father. They watched me and they watched her. There is a house here which is owned by a relative who might rent it to us. I think it would be in the right direction if we moved in there. I feel I've never been a good trapper or hunter; anyway, this kind of work sometimes leaves a woman and her family unprovided for. If I could become a missionary, I'd have a job in the village that would give me steady pay and keep me busy.

The villagers feel that it is ridiculous for Amos to be so jealous. One elderly village woman was most outspoken one evening stating that she felt all the difficulties between Amos and Lilly were due to him. She said, "I do not take his side, as I might do since he is the son of my aunt, and I know Amos' mother-in-law has caused a lot of trouble. She says a lot of things about him that make him mad; but he's been babied all his life by his stepfather; they won't let him grow up. He's never had to take any responsibility like everybody else."

CASE #2 — AKEK

Akek is an eight-year-old North Alaskan Eskimo girl who occasionally without warning throws violent fits. She shouts, she strikes out at others, falls to the floor screaming and kicking, then has trembling and contracting of her arms and legs. The episodes last about five minutes and have occurred several times a year usually during November and January for the past several years.

Akek's family is "very old-fashioned." Her parents are first cousins and speak only Innupiat. They live in a two-room plywood shack. This household is very crowded; the parents sleep on the floor. The family is subjected to much gossip and derisive joking because of their poor economic status. Akek's father cannot provide for his family the meat and clothing considered adequate by most other villagers. Akek is very shy and retiring; even with her peers she says almost nothing, prefers not to be seen; in school she never says a word. Because of joking and mockery from others, the family stay to themselves inside the house. In fact, the parents are said to be afraid of people and they do not allow their children out of the house often.

This family's poor economic condition is generally reflected in their state of poor health. Akek's mother has borne ten children; four of them died in early childhood from respiratory infections. The remaining six children have also been ravaged by respiratory infections and all have long medical histories of chronic drainage from the ears.

School teachers have observed that several of Akek's attacks have occurred after what they assumed was an episode of extreme shyness and embarrassment at being called upon to recite in class. She is so shy and retiring that it is difficult to gain any impression as to her capabilities. Her art work and design copy, however, indicate perceptual abilities and motor abilities which do not differ from peers (see Appendix C). Content and execution of figures on the drawings are age appropriate (see Gesell et al. 1940).

CASE #3 — KAJAT

Kajat is a man who at the age of 52 had his first and only attack of Arctic Hysteria-like behavior. Several months prior to the attack he was noted to be somewhat irritable by the Public Health nurse and by the school teacher. One morning in October he was found by his sons shouting in an irrational way about "a devil" in his house, and had to be restrained from going out of the house with his gun "to shoot caribou" (he said). He broke free and began running around outside of his house, grimacing and shouting that he was seeing devils. The people of the village became alarmed that he might harm himself or others.

He then went to sleep for twenty-four hours. When he woke up he sang hymns loudly and kept stating, "I want my wife." Within forty-eight hours his mentation had apparently returned to normal. A physician who examined him at that time observed that Kajat was not psychotic but suffered from a "hysterical episode," and required no hospitalization or treatment. Kajat and his wife are prosperous through Kajat's hunting. They are considered by most people of the village to be "old-fashioned."

Most significant in precipitating the attack of hysteria was Kajat's depression and inability to feel secure without his wife. He depended on her very much and still does. Several months prior to his attack, his wife was removed from the village for treatment of chronic tuberculosis.

This was their first separation for any extended period. They had depended upon one another for almost forty years. In addition, the nurse had told Kajat that his wife would have one of her lungs removed. He feared she would die.

The operation was performed successfully and Kajat's wife returned to him. He has had no further episodes of Arctic Hysteria.

CASE #4 — MATAMUK

Matamuk is a middle-aged woman who has had periodic episodes of "not knowing what she's doing" during past years. Often these episodes include violent behavior, sometimes directed toward her children. It has been reported that she has bitten them, hit them, and on the latest occasion, attempted to eat the youngest baby. Villagers say this woman "didn't even know what's going on at Christmas time until this last year. It was the first time in her whole life that she knew what it was." Her cousin joked, "Can she really ever be helped? Is she hopeless? I've been watching her out the window; she doesn't know I watch, but I always do. She doesn't even know how to walk. Whenever she walks, she's looking somewhere else but where she's going. Whatever she does she can't remember. She starts something and then she doesn't know what she's doing and has to stop and think."

Matamuk said:

This is the story of my life. We used to live in an old sod house down by the lagoon, but I can't remember that until I was ten years old. There we used to have seal oil lanterns and I burned myself on the nose and forehead. You can see the scars now. I remember something of the old place, but mostly I can't remember; I don't know what happened. We went to the old man's house, that two-story place over there. My father and mother lived over there. I went to school; I used to have lots of spells then. In 1948 I was out of school for seven months with a big spell. I don't remember nothing. I went to Mt. Edgecumbe for high school with a couple of other girls and had to live there in the dormitory for three years without coming home. I had an attack then; I can't remember much about that. One time before then when I was twelve or thirteen years old, they say that I had a fit. I would run down to the beach and try to go into the water without clothes. Another time somebody tells me that when I had my attacks my father kept me in my room and try to put a pillow on me. I had a whole bunch of kids then, one after the other, but didn't get married. Some kids I took care of myself, and my father helped too. Each time I had a kid during the whole pregnancy I can't remember nothing. They say I had my spells then. I got married three years ago and had a little boy, but had my spell during my whole pregnancy with him. After he was born they say I bit him. The last attack was almost a year ago. I had my foot in a cast for October to December. I was in a spell then; I can't remember nothing. They say I kicked my old man, my husband, with my cast on. He got mad, but I can't remember nothing of this.

Last Christmas is the first Christmas that I can remember in my whole life. At Christmas I must have always been in a spell, because I can't remember ever having a Christmas. These things are very strange; no one can explain them. I don't know why I have them.

According to her father, her "spells" started when she was a girl "she would just fall over asleep. But sometimes her eyes would be open, yet she did not seem to see us." These happened several times at church; she would pass out and would have to be carried home, as they could not arouse her. Her father said, "She never knew anything for about an hour; then she would be cross and argue for awhile." Sometimes she would also be irritable before she passed out, but inevitably she was so after she came to. Her father said that in fact she was not unconscious continually, but she would awaken for awhile and then be out again. This went on for at least seven months. During her attack she would have no involuntary movements, but often would just fall over. Matamuk is worried about these spells. She says, "My two younger brothers know a lot more things that happened to me than I do."

The onset of puberty, her mother's death in childbirth, the death of the baby one year later, and her own leaving home and going to Mt. Edgecumbe for high school, all occurred within a period of a year and a half. During the next three years at boarding school she apparently had several other spells, although they were not reported in the medical records. She does state, though, that there were long periods during her stay there that are completely blocked out of her mind. After returning to the village she began to have "kids." She has had six miscarriages and six live births.

Matamuk contends that since she started having children she has had her spells only when pregnant. However, it is claimed by her husband and her father that she has had them on other occasions too. Many of her spells occur after she has gone to bed. Her husband complains that he often becomes quite angry with her because she kicks and bites him in bed. He tries to awaken her when she does it. All of her children, until her last, have been daughters. Her husband had always very much wanted a son. In 1966 she gave birth to her first son. This is the child she tried to eat. In late November 1969, and again in January 1970, she told me of having "night spells." Her husband elaborated that on these occasions she shouted a very high-pitched, eerie sound, jumped up from bed, fell upon him, and began to kick him and bite him in the shoulder. He held her for about ten minutes until she calmed down. He said she was then "very angry at me." Matamuk, however, maintains that she remembers nothing of these events.

CASE #5 — KALAGIK

Kalagik is a nine-year-old boy who has been having fits periodically for several years. At times he appears dazed and weak and will gently fall to the ground. He often does this while playing outside with other children. Other times he will fly into a fury, trying to attack one of the other children. One time he went after a younger brother with a knife, but was restrained by his parents. These attacks are short-lived, lasting only five to ten minutes. Kalagik has no memory for what happens during the attack, but remembers his head "feeling funny" before he blacks out. He also notices that before these attacks his fingers and hands contract, so that he cannot open his hand without prying it open. He face grimaces and twitches during these times.

Kalagik was an irritable infant and cried incessantly. At the age of three he was struck on the head (source of trauma unknown) and was unconscious for about thirty minutes. He also suffered from a chronic ache and discharge from the left ear. In July 1966, when Kalagik was five years old, he "blacked out" and his left arm and left side of his face began twitching. This happened twice during the summer.

His family is very poor by village standards. His father does little else but mine coal from the surface deposits. His mother had a chronic vaginal irritation before and during her pregnancy with Kalagik. Two years before Kalagik's birth, a sister was treated by an itinerant physician for a gonococcal infection. Chronic otitis media has plagued this family for years. The eldest brother had a persistently draining right ear. The next boy had active chronic otitis media, which was treated by the USPHS physician. A sister was treated for right otitis media in 1968. Another sister has badly scarred eardrums bilaterally.

Family Member	Disease	Date of Disease
Father	TB	1957
Mother	Gonorrhea	1/60-9/61
Brother	Right Otitis Drainage	Chronic
Brother	Bilateral Otitis Media	Chronic
Brother	Bilateral Otitis Media	Chronic
Sister	Bilateral Otitis Media	Chronic
Sister	Gonorrhea	1959
	Bilateral Otitis Media	Chronic
Kalagik	Left Otitis Media	12/64
Brother	Bilateral Otitis Media	Chronic

Kalagik's family lives in a single room, ten-by-ten plywood shack with very poor insulation. The room is drafty and heated with an old iron coal stove. His family speaks only Innupiat and attends the Assembly of God church. They are considered poor and "old fashion" by others in the village. In school he is shy and fearful. He is teased by others for being "retarded." Teachers find him a very slow learner. He knows very little English. His art work and design copy indicate severe organic limitations as illustrated by the drawings done by Kalagik and one of his peers (see Appendix C). Execution of figures is crude with gross inability to follow proper angles or straight lines. Animal and human figures are compatible with the productions of a three- or four-year-old child (see Gesell et al. 1940).

CASE #6 — SANRAQ

In August, a sixteen-year-old Eskimo boy who was attending boarding school complained to the nurse that he had a toothache. The next day the tooth was pulled. He complained of feeling faint and dizzy. Shortly thereafter, he appeared to be worried and preoccupied, which lasted throughout the day. The next morning at about 8:00 a.m. he was so dizzy and disoriented that he had to be assisted to his room by several other students. He appeared to stagger when walking. The nurse noted that his color and his temperature and pulse were all normal and he had no other apparent symptoms. He was put to bed in his room. At midnight of the same day, Sanraq ran out of his room without any clothes on, down the stairs, and out of the building. Several boys pursued him. He was staggering, and looked wild. His confused and wild behavior became progressively worse and finally he went into a state of acute physical agitation and excitement. It took five or six people to hold him down. On being restrained he went directly into generalized seizures following which he became relaxed and somnolent but continued to be confused.

Later, after his sensorium had cleared, he was able to state that he did not remember much of what happened to him, but that he knew he was scared and anxious because of "too much pressure in the dormitory." Since leaving home and coming to boarding school one month prior to his episode, this young man had felt extremely homesick and lonely for his friends and relatives in his home village. He was not doing well at school and became the butt of many jokes which primarily came from classmates who had been raised in larger villages or more Westernized communities. This young man felt that others at the boarding school considered him stupid and picked on him because he "didn't know the sex ropes." Sanraq was born and raised in a small village in North Alaska. He was one of seven children and the first to leave home for any extended period of time. He had apparently not been prone to fits, tantrums, or Arctic Hysteria-like behavior in his village. He was not an extremely religious person nor had he been influenced by "old-fashioned ways." His family was prosperous and rather modern by most village standards. On the other hand, he found school and his dormitory situation completely intolerable. He felt that he could not fit in socially with his classmates, and in addition, felt that his teachers "don't set a good example for the way people should live." Sanraq returned to his village because of emotional reasons and academic underachievement during the next month. At home he was criticized for having left school and people wondered what would become of him. However, he was not openly ridiculed or mocked. He has had no recurrences of his hysterical behavior.

CASE #7 — MONTAK

Montak is a thirty-year-old woman who has had periodic episodes of "strange experiences" for the past three years. During her first episode in the winter of 1967, she was acutely assaultive and tried to harm herself. The attack lasted about fifteen minutes. She remembered nothing about the episode. The next year she again had a bout of amnesia lasting about half an hour, during which time she ran from her home into the snow, tearing off her clothing. This winter her husband returned home and heard noises from the back room. There he found his Montak clawing at the bed and looking "quite wild." She said she was talking to her dead mother. In a few minutes she recovered and seemed quite calm and sensible. This time she remembered the event quite well. The next night she saw flashing lights which frightened her but subsided in a few minutes. The flashing lights were again experienced the third night, but have not returned since.

Montak's parents are both dead. She remembers that they were "very old-fashioned people." Father used to tell her stories about the way people used to live, about the power people used to have. She became a Christian in the Assembly of God church because "people here think you're supposed to." She felt that in school she had always been very shy but later in life fell in love with an outsider. People in the village considered the love affair scandalous since they did not approve of the outsider. They felt girls from the village should marry local men. She was the subject of many comments and jokes. Finally, she married the young man, and since then many of the villagers will not speak to her or her husband. Her brothers and sisters have all left the village for one reason or another. With her parents deceased, and her siblings in other places, Montak feels unsupported against the gossip and distrust of the people in her village.

CASE #8 — SAUTAK

Sautak is an eighteen-year-old man, who has had attacks of behavior which an itinerant physician considered to be Arctic Hysteria. The doctor noted the following:

December 1969—Sautak and I met during one of the attacks of what appears to be "Arctic Hysteria." He was brought into the hospital, carried by two other men, screaming at the top of his lungs, his eyes shut tightly, crying and with his arms and legs flailing.

Through conversation, Sautak was able to calm down. In his terror, panic-stricken state he revealed that he had been shot through his left side. According to him the pain was excruciating, which was why he had come to the hospital.

Sautak was overcome by fear. He expressed and displayed his fear that someone was in control of his mind! "They are going to take my mind away. They make me walk when and where and I don't want to go. Somebody's got to control me; I'm getting worse. I can't sleep at night. My hands don't feel like they are mine. My hands, arms and legs go numb sometimes. I am going to die."

After his discharge, and during the next week and a half, Sautak returned on four separate occasions with a repeat of the hysterical outbreaks. I would wind up physically on top of him, holding him down. Occasionally we would wrestle. Except for a very severe fit he was sent home after each outburst.

Interestingly, everytime he blacked out he would pass into a catatonic state of great rigidity. During these times he would begin to squeeze his own fists so tightly that his knuckles would crack. If I put my hands into his, he stopped squeezing and held onto my hands. As soon as I took them out, he would begin cracking his knuckles.

Sautak was born prematurely, but there is no record of how early, with no medical attention other than a midwife. His sister remembers that he was very small at birth. The family concurs that peculiar behavior was noticeable from about age five. He would have nightmares, start shaking (similar to his "fits" now), and sometimes pound the other children's heads against the wall. The mother decided that he would "outgrow it." Until the age of eight, his sister used to sleep with Sautak in the same bed "to get him to get to sleep."

The onset of the blacking out is not definite. There seems to be some confusion in Sautak's mind and the family's as to when they began. However, it is pretty clear that they either started early this summer, or early fall 1968. Sautak thinks that he has passed out at least seven times.

Sautak comes from a family of six children. His father and grandfather were both considered "no good" by the villagers. People considered them to be a family of degenerates and will have little to do with them socially. Older members of the family have left the village and have turned to alcoholism. Sautak is accorded the same derogatory feelings by his peers. In general, he is a loner. He has been unable to make friends with any young women. People usually shake their heads and say "he'll never come to no good, he is like his father and grandfather." References were made frequently by many people to violent fit-like behavior on the part of his father and other older relatives although details could not be adequately ascertained.

CASE #9 — TESOGAT

Tesogat is a twenty-year-old young man who has had episodes of acute, short-lived attacks during which time he feels frightened that spirits and God will kill him. These episodes last several hours. He experiences no amnesia for the attacks. Tesogat stated that while he is "under the spell" he feels that people in his surroundings hate him. He interprets their movements as signs of their hostility toward him.

During the attacks Tesogat acts very frightened and panicky, often rushing out of doors ill clad for the cold weather, apparently to escape from close contact with people indoors. His attacks have occurred in summer and winter months. The latest was January 1970.

His birth was by home delivery with a midwife in attendance. The mother states that according to the midwife, the baby was blue when born. The midwife thought the baby had drunk amniotic fluid before birth. Birth weight was about seven pounds. The baby grew well, and was breast and bottle fed. When six months old he began to have teeth. When a baby he moved very slowly. He was bothered with diarrhea a good part of his early childhood and was trained between two and three years of age. When he was two years old he had swollen glands, earaches, and diarrhea.

For many years Tesogat has talked in his sleep in a language not understood by the family. He seems to be having nightmares and occasionally gets up and walks out of the building without appearing to be fully awake. This behavior at night has caused much concern and irritability of the family because it keeps the rest of the family awake. Recently the parents have kept the door locked because he will wander around outside without his clothes on. When the parents ask him what the trouble is he will not talk and looks afraid to answer.

Tesogat comes from a large family of eight children, his parents are very poor by village standards and speak no English. All of his siblings have had medical histories of severe middle ear disease. Tesogat himself at the age of five had bilateral chronic draining ears and has lost much of his ability to hear. Because of this, he has frequently impressed others with his unresponsiveness. Most consider him dull or retarded; he was troublesome in school because he could not respond or learn in class. Classmates frequently made fun of his dumb expression when he would be asked a question. Tesogat has become very religious in the Assembly of God church, but states that he fears God will hate him and despise him because he can do nothing. He states that he knows nothing and can never be a man in his village, or have a wife because he does not know what to do. He is frightened about living in the village, but going out of the community to another place such as Fairbanks or Anchorage frightens him even more. He says, "in a small place everybody knows what you are doing; everybody watches you; everybody sees your mistakes. I make mistakes and they hate me."

See Appendix C for a note he wrote to me shortly before his last attack.

CASE #10 — NIRIK

Nirik is a young Eskimo woman who for the past six years has had episodic fits of unmanageable fury. These fits last about thirty minutes, during which time she breaks furniture and windows, assaults members of her family, shouts obscenities, and has on occasion tried to rip off her clothing. She has amnesia for the attacks. The episodes occur primarily in the winter and are often precipitated by an "argument with a man." She was seen by an itinerant physician in March 1970 in a state of acute agitation. He felt she suffered from "hysteria."

Nirik's father was a nomadic hunter, and her mother accompanied him in living off the land. She was left with relatives when she was a baby because she could not be cared for adequately when her parents moved about the northern tundra trapping and hunting. She was cared for by a paternal uncle and his family, not seeing her parents again until age thirteen. At that time they returned to the village permanently. Father collected social security and gathered his children together in his own household. Relations, however, became extremely strained for Nirik when her father began to make sexual advances toward her. She felt repulsed by the idea, yet did not want to leave the household because "my parents are getting old and they need my help." She seems preoccupied by her father's sexuality yet fears it.

Her feelings toward her parents are tremendously ambivalent. Significant in her past history is the fact that she was raped by two boys at age eighteen and raped again last year. She states that because of these episodes plus experiences she had with "my own daddy" she has very poor relationships with males. She complains of feeling tense and anxious whenever she is in the presence of a man. When she has gone out on dates she has become filled with fear any time a boy approaches her for a kiss or to hold her hand.

Others in the village consider her odd and laugh at her "frigidity." She, however, has been unable to overcome her fears. At an early age when she would become acutely excited she would begin to hyperventilate. This would cause her to become dizzy and she would feel that she was losing control of her behavior. She learned to blow into a bag and breathe the exhaled air in as a means to "clear ·my head." Appearing outdoors in the village now fills her with panic. She states that when others laugh at her she cannot think—"my mind gets cloudy."

She has several siblings who have gone to live in Fairbanks. Her brothers are alcoholics and have led greatly disrupted lives; her sisters have turned to prostitution and alcoholism. She states that as she sees it she would have gone that route too because "it was a lot of fun." However, in the tenth grade in high school, she "learned about Christ." She converted to the Baptist religion and has remained close to the church through the years. Quite consciously she seems ambivalent about moral ideas. On the one hand, she smiles in almost a seductive way when speaking about the drinking and carousing of her sisters; and on the other, she becomes tearful and shameful when she speaks about how this behavior breaks the ways Christ taught people to live and what Christian people expect of you.

Her last attack was preceded by an aura of ringing in the ears, dizziness and a dry mouth. This was accompanied with a degree of hyperventilation. After that she stated that she blacked out mentally and remembered virtually nothing that occurred to her or how long she had been under the spell.

SUMMARY OF FINDINGS

The events in the life histories of these ten cases which may be related to their Arctic Hysteria-like behavior are illustrated in Table IX.

TABLE IX. LIFE HISTORY EVENTS

	Case Number									
	1	2	3	4	5	6	7	8	9	10
Adopted or abandoned by parents	X	0	0	0	X	0	X	0	0	X
Influenced by "old-fashioned" elders	X	X	X	X	X	0	X	?	X	X
Shamanistic associations	X	?	X	?	?	0	X	?	?	?
Religious or supernatural experiences	X	?	?	X	?	0	X	0	X	X
Sexual or spouse jealousy	X	—	0	0	—	X	0	0	0	0
Shamed by peers	X	X	0	X	X	X	X	X	X	X
Shy and suspicious of peers	X	X	0	X	X	X	X	X	X	X
Loss of significant support of wife, etc.	X	0	X	0	X	X	X	0	0	0
Family ridiculed and ostracized from village	0	X	0	0	X	0	0	X	X	0
Family history of hysterical behavior	X	0	0	0	0	0	0	X	0	0

X = presence of event in life history of individual
0 = absence of event

The most consistently occurring events in the life histories of the ten North Alaskan Eskimos who manifested Arctic Hysteria-like behavior were: (1) being raised by tradition-oriented elders who in many cases related experiences of past human powers or shamanism; (2) having themselves felt religiously or supernaturally inspired; (3) having been shamed and ridiculed by elders and peers which frequently resulted in a shy, retiring, suspicious characterological position. Many wished to escape from the village, yet felt too strange and insecure going anywhere else. They were essentially double-bound in a conflict-ridden social situation. Most felt alone in facing their social difficulties after the death or illness of, or abandonment by, close relatives.

VIII. The Calcium Hypothesis

EARLIER WE NOTED that several authors had considered deficiencies of calcium in the Eskimo diet as a potential source of metabolic disturbance manifesting itself in the Arctic Hysterias. Høygaard (1941:72), for example, found gross deficiencies of calcium intake in the diets of the Greenland Eskimos, and had reported their extreme tendency toward hysterical attacks. Later, Wallace reasoned that low calcium intake plus reduced vitamin D_3 synthesis during the minimal ultraviolet radiation levels of the winter may have been sufficient to render the Eskimo hypocalcemic at these times.

In such a precarious physiological state, those Eskimos who are inclined to become acutely anxious may precipitate the Arctic Hysteria attack by breathing rapidly or hyperventilating. This further lowers blood levels of free calcium by raising the pH. We summarized this possible series of events in a recent article (Katz and Foulks 1970) by using a model similar to that given in Figure 6.

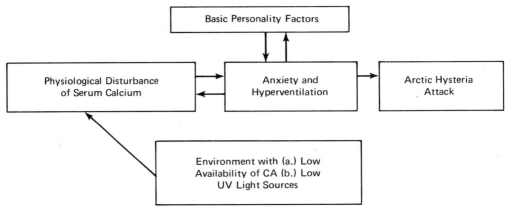

Figure 6.

Wallace (1961:271) has recently pointed out that the hysteria once common in America and Europe also may have been a result of physiological disturbances of calcium metabolism. He cites evidence that between 1880 and 1895 there were epidemics of tetany among the working class people of Vienna, Paris, and other European urban areas. These epidemics were not recognized as hypocalcemic episodes because methods of assaying serum calcium had not yet been established at that time. Milk, however, was absent from the diet of the working class urban European in the nineteenth century, and "Victorian" styles in especially women's clothing did not permit skin exposure to sunlight. Rickets, tetany, and (as proposed by Wallace) hysteria were the prevalent conditions resulting from this inavailability of calcium. The discovery of the value of sunlight, milk, and vitamin D_3-containing foods, and the general amelioration of social conditions during the early 1900s, was accompanied by a rapid decrease in rickets, tetany, and hysteria.

Freud, of course, derived many of his psychoanalytic insights (the "unconscious," infantile sexuality, etc.) from clinical experience with hysterical women in the later years of the nineteenth century. Freud did sense that these patients possessed some constitutional proclivity toward hysterical overreactions. He did not pursue this line of reasoning, however, perhaps because the methods to do so were at that time undeveloped. Instead, he concentrated his attentions on the fantasies and mental events which occurred in these patients which ultimately led to the development of psychoanalytic theory. What role hypocalcemia played in determining the symptomatology of Freud's patients is of course impossible to determine at this time. However, the persistance of hysterical symptoms in many non-Western societies offers the possibility of testing the calcium hypothesis in at least these circumstances. The Arctic Hysterias among the North Alaskan Eskimo provides such an opportunity.

In this chapter we will examine the calcium hypothesis in more detail by outlining the factors involved in calcium homeostasis, and how the central nervous system is affected by perturbations in levels of this ion. In addition, the calcium hypothesis was tested on the cases of Arctic Hysteria reported in the previous section. Calcium levels in all subjects were determined and compared with norms established recently in a north Alaskan Eskimo village. Results of this study will be presented in detail in a later section.

HYPOCALCEMIA AND THE SYMPTOMS OF THE ARCTIC HYSTERIAS

In a recent review of the medical literature, Denko and Kaelbling (1962) collected 268 case histories of individuals who suffered hypoparathyroidism, a condition resulting in hypocalcemia. They pointed out that this condition has been seldom considered in the differential diagnosis of psychiatric disorders, and went on to enumerate symptoms which they found to be commonly associated with this condition. The criterion for diagnosing hypocalcemia was at least one serum calcium determination below 9 mg% (Denko and Kaelbling 1962:13).

They found that cases fell into five categories:

1. Intellectual Impairment
2. Organic Brain Syndrome
3. Schizophrenia or Manic-Depressive Psychotic Symptoms
4. Neurotic Symptoms, such as Hysteria, Hypochondriasis, etc.
5. Undiagnosable psychiatric symptoms, which included depression, nervousness, irritability, children with tantrums and night terrors.

The distribution of these categories was as follows:

	Female	Male	Total
1. Intellectual Impairment	21	32	54*
2. Organic Brain Syndrome	67	25	93*
3. Psychosis	27	1	29*
4. Neurosis	23	9	33*
5. Undiagnosed	42	15	59*

*Cases included where no sex was mentioned

Acute episodes of hysterical behavior characterized cases in many of these diagnostic categories. The behavior, as described, shares many features in common with the Arctic Hysterias. Below are examples from such cases abstracted from Denko and Kaelbling's monograph (1962:40-57).

Case	Age	Description	Diagnosis
41	28	"Paranoid, suspicious"	Intellectual Impairment
44	38	"Episodic rage & drowsiness"	,,
53	16	"Manic, disoriented, fearful"	Organic Brain Syndrome
58	29	"Brief periods of confusion"	,,
60	30	"Episodic disorientation"	,,
68	43	"Spells of agitation"	,,
71	58	"Episodic confusion"	,,
72	58	"Attacks associated with emotional strain"	,,
78	9	"Attacks resembled DT's"	,,
92	?	"Explosive, labile"	,,
93	?	"Manic-hysteriform picture"	
98	38	"Several manic episodes lasting several hours"	Psychosis
104	?	"Episodic psychosis"	,,
108	28	"Hysterical behavior"	,,
223	39	"Hysteria"	,,
224	39	"2 attacks of maniacal excitement"	,,
229	53	"Grand mal epilepsy with hysterical component"	,,
237	27	"Spells like daze-hysterical"	Neurosis
238	30	"Hysteria"	,,
240	31	". . . Hysteria"	,,
241	33	"Tetany when under emotional stress"	,,
243	39	". . . Hysteria"	,,
245	56	". . . Hysterical"	,,
246	56	"Tetany under tension—hyperventilation"	,,
109	31	"Hysterical attacks"	,,
110	36	"Hysterical complaints"	,,
112	47	"Tetanic attacks provoked by emotion"	,,
116	15	"Hysteric"	,,
119	33	"Conversion hysteria"	,,
120	38	"Episodic depression, emotional lability"	,,
127	2	"Rages, night terrors"	Undiagnosed
135	28	"Nervousness with pregnancies"	,,
155	39	"Highly excited, hyperventilating"	,,

CALCIUM AND ESKIMO DIET

The symptoms of the Arctic Hysterias are thus compatible with a diagnosis of hypocalcemia. This diagnosis is made even more plausible by the findings of Høygaard (1941) which indicated severe deficiencies in dietary intake of calcium. Stefansson (1945:286-288) noted that the exclusively carnivorous diet of the Eskimo might be very low in calcium. He decided to experiment himself with such a diet, and for one year lived on an all meat diet in New York. Chemists at the Russell Sage Institute studied Stefansson and his friend, Anderson, during the year and felt that they did not get enough calcium. At the end of the year, however, the two subjects exhibited no evidence of calcium deficiency. The nutritionists postulated that perhaps they had not been on the calcium deficient diet long enough for clinical evidence to appear.

More recently a nutritional survey was conducted in Alaska by Heller and Scott (1956-61). They collected a total of 4840 diet records of about seven days' duration on a seasonal basis for both sexes and all age levels from nine Eskimo and two Athabascan villages. The villages included:

Northwest	1.	Point Hope	Innuit
	2.	Noatak	Innuit
	3.	Shishmaref	Innuit
	4.	Shungnak	Innuit
Southwest	5.	Akiak	Yuit
	6.	Napaskiak	Yuit
	7.	Kasigluk	Yuit
	8.	Hooper Bay	Yuit
	9.	Nowtok	Yuit
Interior	10.	Allakaket	Athabascan
	11.	Huslia	Athabascan

From these records the data were converted by machine calculation into mean daily intakes of eleven major nutrients (calories, protein, fat, carbohydrate, calcium, iron, vitamin A, thiamin, riboflavin, niacin, and ascorbic acid). These were then compared to the National Research Council (1958) recommendations of 0.8 gms for adults and 1 gm for children.

The mean daily calcium intake levels among Eskimos and Athabascans were considerably below those recommended by the National Research Council for all age groups and genders. Three-fourths or more of the diets for each age and sex were deficient. The ranges in mean intake level, however, were extremely wide (see Table X).

TABLE X. CALCIUM INTAKES ON ALASKAN ESKIMO AND INDIAN DIETS*

Age-Sex Category	Number of Records	Mean Daily Intake (mg)	Intake Range (mg)	Percent under NRC (4)
Adult male 20-60 yrs.	746	576	399-3813	75
Adult male 60+ yrs.	112	461	381-2010	87
Adult female 20-60 yrs.	633	481	254-2197	87
Adult female 60+ yrs.	120	322	87-886	95
Adult female pregnant	121	561	279-3115	97
Adult female lactating	193	531	197-2027	99
Male 13-19 yrs.	303	660	372-1880	96
Female 13-19 yrs.	298	580	381-2010	97
Schoolchild 7-12 yrs.	916	684	250-1936	80
Preschoolchild 2-6 yrs.	843	641	33-2319	85

*All areas and villages, all seasons, by age and sex
(Heller and Scott 1956-61:47)

"The extreme variance between low and high calcium intakes in all villages might be interpreted, at least in part, as evidence of the variable importance given to milk as an item in the young child's diet" (Heller and Scott 1956-61:47). Milk is, of course, an imported food, requiring not only an orientation toward the Western diet, but cash outlay as well. Levels according to village are given in Table XI.

TABLE XI. PROPORTION OF CALCIUM FROM LOCAL AND IMPORTED FOODS*

Village	Number of Records	Mean Daily Intake	Local Foods	Import Foods	School Lunch	Vitamins	Mixed Foods
Innuit Eskimo							
Noatak	462	661	81	533	40	—	7
Point Hope	362	652	41	532	76	—	3
Shishmaref	372	634	68	448	112	—	6
Shungnak	285	468	75	342	42	2	7
Yuit Eskimo							
Akiak	228	582	77	416	79	—	10
Napaskiak	422	514	108	332	69	—	5
Kasigluk	351	649	132	463	43	—	11
Hooper Bay	1212	607	105	453	44	—	5
Newtok	247	763	368	341	54	—	0
Athabascan							
Huslia	369	657	39	609	—	—	9
Allakaket	257	629	52	481	79	9	8

*By village in milligrams
(Heller and Scott 1956-61:49)

They estimated the probable intake level in aboriginal times by comparing the calcium content of adult female diets at Hooper Bay (southwestern Eskimo) and Pt. Hope (northern Eskimo). Hooper Bay women obtained more than three times as much calcium from local foods, chiefly from whole blackfish and needlefish. Calcium intake must have been still lower in the past in the Pt. Hope diet where these particular fish are not available and other calcium sources are limited. Even at Hooper Bay the above-mentioned fish sources are not continuously available throughout the year, nor are they so abundant that significant supplies can be dried or otherwise preserved for off-season use (Heller and Scott 1956-61:50). Levels for mean daily intake and availability of calcium from local foods and import foods are consistently low for northwestern Alaskan Innuit villages.

In summary, it was discovered that protein and niacin intakes were generally high; 75% or more of the diets were low in calories, calcium, and ascorbic acid; 33% were low in vitamin A and thiamine; 25% were low in riboflavin. Extremely high mean daily intake of iron was recorded for the Innuit villages; but 33% of adolescents, pregnant and lactating women, women over sixty, and preschool children from Yuit villages had inadequate intake. These people depend more on fish in their diets than do the northern Eskimos who hunt caribou and sea mammals, sources of blood and red meat, which contain iron.

CALCIUM REGULATION IN HUMANS

It has been proposed that low serum calcium can affect the human central nervous system, resulting in behavior remarkably similar to that described in the Arctic Hysterias of the Eskimo. Furthermore, there is evidence that the diet of the Eskimo is generally deficient in calcium. The role of calcium in the physiology of man and the possible mechanisms through which this cation might affect the central nervous system will now be discussed.

Figure 7 indicates the many physiological functions of calcium in the human body. Calcium is the most prevalent cation in the body. It is involved in bone formation, muscle contraction, and several steps of blood clotting. Two of its other functions have direct relevance to the adequate function of the nervous system. It is involved in membrane permeability to other ions, both during the process of muscle contraction and, as is shown at the right of Figure 7, in the conduction of neural impulse. At the synapse or nerve ending, calcium is involved in the regulation of the amount of synaptic transmitter agent, such as acetylocholine, released upon stimulation. The net effect of lowering calcium ion concentration is to increase neural excitability. Clinically, we see this manifested as an increased neuromuscular irritability. This results in an increased reflex activity, and in the more exteme case presents as tetany. A classic sign of tetany is carpopedal muscular spasm, which has also been present in past descriptions of the Arctic Hysterias.

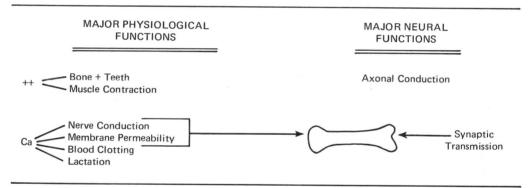

Figure 7. The major physiological functions of calcium in humans (Katz and Foulks 1970:300).

Figure 8 indicates how calcium is regulated and compartmentalized in the body. There are three factors important in calcium homeostasis. First is PTH, or parathormone, which is secreted by the parathyroid glands in response to hypocalcemia. Next is TCT, or calcitonin, which is a hormone secreted from the thyroid gland during hypocalcemia (Rasmussen and Pechet 1970). And last is vitamin D, which forms part of the diet and/or is synthesized by the action of ultraviolet light from the sun upon chemical (sterol) precursors at the level of the skin. This vitamin is fat soluble and may be stored in the liver up to several months. Calcium is ingested as part of the diet. The richest sources are milk and dairy products. However, in a nutritional analysis of calcium, it is not enough to know the total amount of calcium consumed; other important chemical and physiological factors must be considered. For example, phytate, a chemical contained in a variety of cereal grains, and oxalates found in other plants, may form complexes with calcium in the gastrointestinal system and prevent its absorption. Furthermore, the amount of phosphates consumed or available for absorption also plays a role in the amount of calcium which can be absorbed. Recently, Phang et al. (1969) have demonstrated that even the rate of consumption of calcium is also a very important variable in its absorption. Once in the gastrointestinal tract, calcium is absorbed through the action of first vitamin D and then PTH. This order is important, since PTH is ineffective in the absence of vitamin D, whereas vitamin D is effective alone. Calcium, which is not absorbed or is passively secreted in digestive juices, is excreted in the feces.

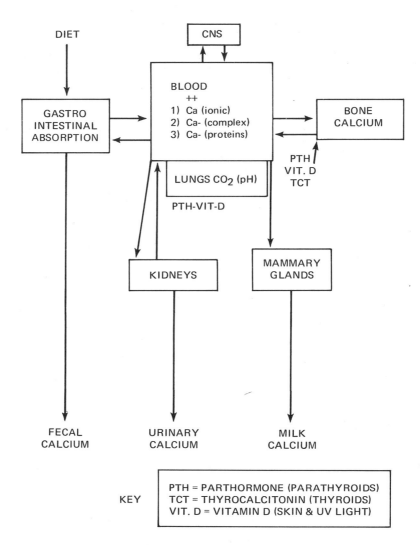

Figure 8. Calcium ion homeostasis with all of the major compartments and the known control mechanisms (Katz and Foulks 1970:300).

In the bloodstream, calcium exists in three forms: free ionic calcium which is the physiologically active form; a form complexed to various metabolic intermediates such as lactate and citrate; and a form bound to serum proteins, especially albumin. It has been established that the calcium ion concentration is actively involved in the physiological reactions shown in the figure above. Of the protein-bound and complexed forms, the former is the larger and may be the more important since albumin binds calcium in a manner that varies directly with pH. This brings into play the regulatory role of the lungs which help to regulate (blood) pH indirectly by ventilatory loss of carbon dioxide. For example, hyperventilation produces loss of CO_2, a rise in pH and consequently an increased protein binding of "free" ionic calcium. Subjective anxiety often precipitates rapid breathing which in turn results in decreasing ionized calcium in the blood. The kidneys are also involved in regulating calcium levels. Both PTH and vitamin D act upon the mechanism of renal resorption to raise the concentration of calcium in the blood. That calcium which is not resorbed is excreted in the urine. Another source of calcium loss very important in the female is in milk during lactation. Bone, of course, is extremely important as a reservoir of calcium for structural and regulatory purposes. Here vitamin D and PTH act to resorb bone salts and raise serum calcium levels. However, another hormone, TCT, acts to block the action of PTH on bone, but without influencing the kidneys.

THE ROLE OF PHOSPHATE

Total serum phosphorous amounts to 12 mg%, of this about 3 mg% is inorganic phosphate. This fraction is completely ionized and under hormonal control. In children, the level of inorganic phosphate is considerably higher, approximately 6 mg%. There exists a reciprocal relationship between the concentration of calcium and phosphate in the blood. Thus any condition which alters the concentration of one ion will correspondingly cause an opposite change in concentration in the other. Normally, parathormone regulates the ratio of these ions. It has been determined that the "calcium-phosphorous product" is a useful index of the degree of calcification in severe calcium deficiencies. The value is low for example in rickets, and is normally elevated in young growing children. The normal value is 30-40 mg% for adults and 40-55 mg% for children.

IONIZED CALCIUM AND THE HUMAN CENTRAL NERVOUS SYSTEM

The general mechanisms which regulate calcium and ultimately determine levels of this cation in the serum have been discussed above. The effect of calcium ion on the central nervous system will now be examined.

It has been shown that decrease in ionic calcium surrounding an axon results in (1) a decreased electrical resistance of the axonal membrane, (2) an increased membrane permeability to sodium, (3) a decrease in rheobase, and (4) a decrease in accommodation. This leads to an increase of the critical membrane potential (Ecrit.), with a decrease in resting membrane potential (RP) of the neuron. The next result is an increased excitability of the nerve (Brink 1954; Mountcastle 1968).

Decreased extracellular calcium can also increase axonal permeability to potassium and sodium by uncoupling from the cell membrane thus altering its stability. The property is shared by other divalent cations such as magnesium.

Calcium also directly affects activities at neural junctions. Acetylcholine is a neurohumeral substance found in neurons near their synaptic junctions. During the process of neural transmission acetylcholine is released at the synaptic junction. Calcium has been shown to regulate the release of acetylcholine. Thus, altering the level of ionized calcium would affect the release of acetylcholine, which in turn affects neuronal activity. Level of consciousness, motor behavior, and psychological state are, of course, functions of overall brain neuronal activity. When the ratio of extracellular to intracellular ionized calcium becomes lowered, as in hypocalcemia, cellular binding of acetylcholine is inhibited, thus releasing this substance with resulting neuronal hyperexcitability (Grenell and Romero 1970).

Calcium ion also plays a major role in triggering the production of certain intracellular proteins which alter the qualitative characteristics of the neurohumeral transmitter substance. Calcium ion stimulates DNA, the basic genetic material to produce a specific RNA, which in turn causes the amino acids in the cell to form a chain of a specific kind of protein. When this protein is formed, a transmitter is automatically released from the cell in a particular amount. This mechanism has been proposed as possibly accounting for spontaneous firing of neural circuits which are manifest as an experience of memory, that is, signals to the central nervous system unprovoked by external stimuli entering through the sense organs. Altering calcium ion concentration in either a high or low direction inhibits this DNA-RNA . . .response. This inhibition may account for the intellectual impairment, disorientation, and memory loss which often characterize hypocalcemic individuals (Grenell and Romero 1970).

Evidence for calcium deficiency in the diet of North Alaskan Eskimos has been presented, and the possible consequent mechanisms resulting in altered central nervous system functioning has been explored. Several questions remain: (1) What is the actual distribution of serum calcium levels in the Innuit? (2) What is the distribution of these levels in Innuit who experience acute psychotic episodes? (3) Do these levels vary seasonally because of change of diet or availability of UV, or other changes in biological rhythms?

SERUM CALCIUM LEVELS IN NORTH ALASKAN ESKIMOS

A North Alaskan Eskimo community of Wainwright was recently studied by a group of scientists under the International Biological Program (Laughlin 1970; Milan 1968). Among the many physiological measurements performed on the population of this village were determinations of serum calcium and phosphate. The results of this survey are summarized in Figures 9 and 10.

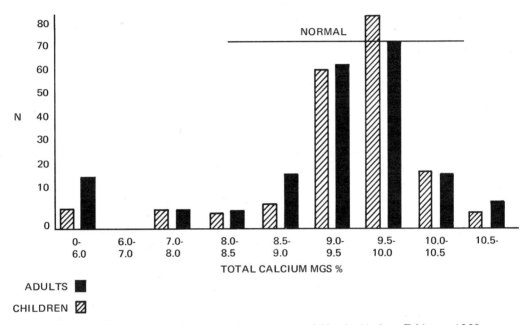

Figure 9. Distribution of serum calcium levels of North Alaskan Eskimos, 1968.

The bar graphs indicate that calcium and phosphate levels are within the normal range for the majority of the population (Mean $Ca^{\#}$ = 9.31, PO_4 = 4.3). Some individuals, however, did demonstrate lower than normal levels of serum calcium. Subsequent surveys were conducted in this village in 1969 and 1970. The results of these surveys have not as yet been published. However, Dr. Frank Pauls, of the Wisconsin State Laboratory of Hygiene, who had originally conducted this study, has made his unanalyzed data available for our study. Figure 11 indicates the results of our analysis.

Our analysis indicated that calcium serum levels were within the normal range for the majority of the population of this village during the summer of 1968 (Pauls et al. 1969). Thus, in spite of low availability of calcium in food sources, the majority of the Eskimo population in North Alaska has maintained normal levels of this essential cation. It should be pointed out, however, that the blood samples were drawn each year during the summer months when sunlight is plentiful. Sunlight provides the opportunity for autosynthesis of vitamin D from ultraviolet solar radiation. The availability of vitamin D, therefore, may render physiological serum calcium levels during the summer months. Recently a winter survey was taken by these same investigators. The results as yet have not been analyzed.

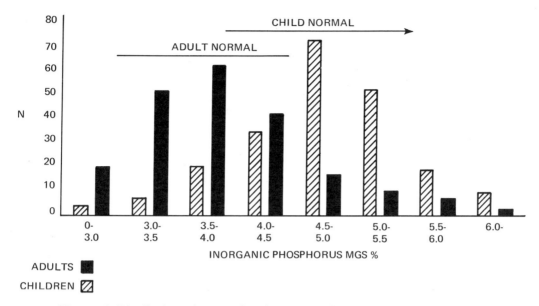

Figure 10. Distribution of serum phosphate levels of North Alaskan Eskimos, 1968.

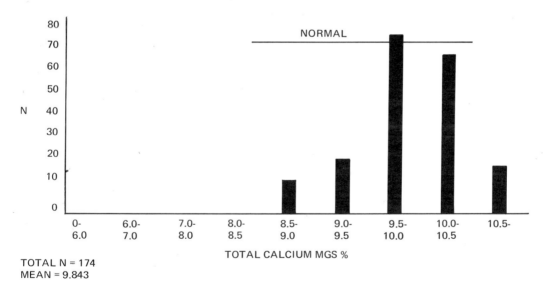

Figure 11. Distribution of serum calcium levels of North Alaskan Eskimos, 1970.

SERUM CALCIUM LEVELS IN ARCTIC HYSTERIA

10 cc of blood were collected without venous stasis in Vacutainer tubes (Becton-Dickenson, Rutherford, New Jersey) from our ten North Alaskan Eskimos who had manifested Arctic Hysteria-like behavior. All subjects had been fasting over eight hours prior to the venipuncture. After sitting for fifteen minutes at room temperature, the blood was centrifuged at 2000 rpm; 5 cc

of serum were then transferred to a small polyethelene container and frozen immediately. Specimens were then analyzed for total calcium by fluorometry using the method of Kepner and Hercules (1963) modified for the Techicon Autoanalyzer. (Special gratitude is extended to Dr. Peter Morrison and William Galster from the Institute of Arctic Biology, University of Alaska College, for their contributions in the support and the analysis of serum calcium in our subjects.) We were able to follow several individuals throughout seasonal changes. Others were either unavailable at certain times of the year, or presented Arctic Hysteria-like behavior only in the later stages of our study. The results are presented in Table XII.

TABLE XII. TOTAL SERUM CALCIUM IN MGS%

Season		July, '68	July, '69	Sept, '69	Nov, '69	Jan, '70	March, '70	Mean
Subject	#1	9.3	—	—	9.7	10.7	9.2	9.7
	#2	10.0	9.4	—	—	—	—	9.7
	#3	9.2	8.9	—	—	—	—	9.05
	#4	9.8	9.5	9.1	9.9	9.8	9.1	9.8
	#5	9.3	—	—	7.5	—	—	8.4
	#6	8.8	—	—	—	—	—	8.8
	#7	—	—	—	—	8.5	—	8.5
	#8	—	—	—	9.8	9.4	—	9.6
	#9	—	—	—	—	9.0	—	9.0
	#10	—	—	—	9.6	10.0	—	9.8
Mean		9.4	9.3	9.1	9.3	9.5	9.15	9.4

Case #5 was hypocalcemic in November 1969, but normocalcemic July 1968. The remaining subjects maintained normal levels of total serum calcium throughout the change of seasons. There were no decreases in levels as expected during the dark winter months. The mean levels for this group did not differ significantly from the levels established for the North Alaskan Eskimo population in general. While within the physiological range, the serum calcium of cases #3, 4, 5, 6, and 7 were on the low side, and it is not inconceivable that hyperventilation or alterations of calcium circadian rhythms could precipitate hypocalcemic states. Unfortunately, we were not able to collect serum from any of our subjects just prior to or during an attack. These levels, therefore, only represent the state of our subjects from one to fourteen days following an episode of Arctic Hysteria-like behavior.

PHOSPHOROUS

Serum inorganic phosphate was determined at the same time as total calcium for several of our subjects. Phosphate and calcium-phosphorous product did not deviate from the range of normal (see Table XIII).

IONIZED CALCIUM

It has been pointed out that calcium exists in human serum in three fractions. Total calcium determinations reflect the summation of the three fractions. The biologically active portion of serum calcium is ionized. It is only this fraction which is available for direct effect on the cells of

TABLE XIII. TOTAL CALCIUM AND INORGANIC PHOSPHATE MGS%, INNUITS WITH ARCTIC HYSTERIA-LIKE BEHAVIOR.

Subject	July, 1968			July, 1969		
	Total Ca	Inorganic PO_4	$Ca\text{-}PO_4$ Product (30-46 adult) (40-55 child)	Total Ca	Inorganic PO_4	$Ca\text{-}PO_4$ Product (30-46 adult) (40-55 child)
Adult #1	9.3	4.3	40.0	—	—	—
Child #2	10.0	4.4	40.4	9.4	4.7	34.1
Adult #3	9.2	3.6	33.1	8.9	3.5	31.2
Adult #4	9.8	4.0	39.2	9.5	3.0	28.5
Child #5	9.3	5.8	53.9	—	—	—
Adolescent #6	8.8	5.3	46.6	—	—	—

TABLE XIV. ULTRAFILTERABLE AND TOTAL CALCIUM IN THE SERUM OF INNUIT

	Total Calcium		Ultrafilterable Calcium	
	Subjects with Arctic Hysteria	Normals	Subjects with Arctic Hysteria	Normals
Mean	9.2286	9.3238	4.8071	4.7143
High	10.0	10.2	5.5	5.6
Low	7.5	7.6	4.4	3.3
S.D.	0.7363	0.6833	0.2973	0.5063
$\dfrac{Ca^{++}}{Ca} \times 100$			51%	46%
t	0.3916		0.6174	

the nervous system. Methods of directly assaying ionized calcium have not been established until recently. Farese et al. (1970) discussed a method which separates protein-bound calcium from ionized calcium and small amounts of calcium bound to inorganic molecules. Since the particular force of our study is the effect of calcium ion on the central nervous system, we felt it necessary to determine levels of this ultrafilterable portion of calcium.

For this purpose, the sera of our ten subjects were compared with twenty-one healthy controls matched for ethnic group and time of venipuncture (see Table XIV). Blood was collected by the methods outlined for total calcium. Serum was diluted in phosphate buffer (pH 7.40), and ionized calcium was separated with the Centriflo (Amicon Corporation) high flux ultrafiltration membrane (Farese et al. 1970). This fraction of calcium was then analyzed by fluorometry. Normal values of ionized calcium determined by ultrafiltration methods range from forty-five to fifty-seven percent of total calcium (Henry 1964).

Our subjects and the matched group of normals showed no significant differences in total calcium or ultrafilterable calcium levels. Mean total calcium was within the range of normal for both groups; and percent of the ultrafilterable portion was also normal.

MAGNESIUM

Magnesium is another divalent cation whose action is related to that of calcium. Its role in the physiological functioning of the body and central nervous system is only recently being understood. Deficiencies of magnesium produce neuromuscular irritability similar to hypocalcemia, including psychosis, tetany, seizures, and positive Chvostik's and Trousseau's signs (see Appendix E)(Vallee 1958:475; Davidson 1963:1191; Wintrobe et al. 1970:1370). Magnesium deficiencies may result from lack of vegetables in the diet, from states of intestinal malabsorption, or from severe alcoholism (*Annals NY Academy of Science*, Vol. 162, 1969).

Vegetables are relatively infrequent items in Eskimo diet; enteric infections are relatively common; and alcoholism is not unknown. And, since magnesium deficiency so closely mimics the symptoms of hypocalcemia, it was decided to examine several of the individuals who manifested Arctic Hysteria-like behavior. Seven of our subjects were matched with twenty normals from the same villages and for the time of venipuncture (see Table XV). Serum was prepared according to the methods outlined for total calcium determination. Magnesium concentrations were analyzed with the Perkin-Elmer model 303 Atomic Absorption spectrophotometer.

TABLE XV. TOTAL SERUM MAGNESIUM MGS%

	Subjects with Arctic Hysteria	Normals
# 1	2.1	
4	2.5	
5	2.4	
7	0.75	
8	2.5	
9	2.5	
10	3.1	
Mean	2.2643	2.1600
High	3.1	3.8
Low	0.75	
S.D.	0.7307	1.0283
t	0.2460	

The physiological range for serum magnesium is normally 1.6-2.6 mg% (2.1 average). Mean levels for both subjects and normals were within these limits, and did not differ from one another significantly. One individual with Arctic Hysteria-like behavior did demonstrate an exceptionally low serum magnesium level (Case #7=0.75 mg%). This individual is presently being investigated in more detail in order to elucidate the causes for this.

SUMMARY

Several articles have suggested that the Arctic Hysterias may represent behaviors associated with hypocalcemia. Lack of adequate dietary calcium and low levels of vitamin D synthesis during the Arctic winter were proposed as causes for this condition. Our analysis of several serological surveys of the North Alaskan Eskimo do not support the notion that this population is unable to maintain normal calcium levels. Serum total calcium determination of ten Innuit who manifested Arctic Hysteria-like behaviors revealed normocalcemic levels during all seasons of the year. However, several subjects demonstrated calcium levels which were decidedly on the low side of normal. Levels of the ultrafilterable fraction of serum calcium was also determined. These levels were again within normal limits and did not differ significantly from a group of matched controls. The subjects also maintained serum inorganic phosphate levels within the normal range.

Our studies, therefore, indicate that the behaviors seen in the Arctic Hysterias are not accompanied by states of chronic hypocalcemia. This finding does not exclude the possibility, however, that hyperventilation with anxiety, or alterations in calcium rhythms, might play a role in precipitating the attacks, especially in view of low normal levels in several subjects.

The ability of the Eskimo to generally maintain normal levels of calcium in spite of dietary deficiencies needs explanation, however. It has recently been demonstrated that there is an increased calcium absorption with increase in protein intake, presumably, because of the formation of a soluble complex with amino acids (Mountcastle 1968:940). Thus the high protein diet of the Eskimo may allow more efficient utilization of the low amounts of calcium normally ingested.

In addition, serum magnesium was measured in most of our subjects, since the action of this cation resembles so closely that of calcium in the central nervous system. The mean levels for the group of subjects was normal and did not differ significantly for a group of co-villagers who were free from hysterical symptoms. One individual, however, demonstrated hypomagnesemic levels which is presently being further investigated. Mendelson et al. (1969) have recently reported correlations between depressed serum magnesium levels and the appearance of alcohol withdrawal signs and symptoms. Poor dietary intake during prolonged drinking plus enhanced urinary excretion of magnesium when blood ethonol levels are rising combine to produce magnesium deficiency.

IX. Calcium Rhythms

ABOVE THE ARCTIC CIRCLE daylight varies dramatically with the changing seasons. In late June the sun never sets but moves 360° around the horizon. In late December the sun never comes above the horizon and offers only a deep red glow to the sky for several hours. During autumn and spring the transition of sunlight is rapid. In temperate zones of the world, man is able to synchronize his activity and sleep cycles with the daily cycle of light-dark. Human physiology has in many respects become dependent on consistent, external synchronizers such as light-dark diurnal rhythms for maintaining stable internal biological rhythms. In the Arctic diurnal light-dark cycles vary rapidly and dramatically throughout the year. Arctic man is thus subjected to inconsistent light-dark cycles in the spring and fall, and no cycling at all in mid-summer and mid-winter. Recent investigations among the Eskimos of North Alaska have revealed that these light-dark inconsistencies seriously perturb certain diurnal physiological rhythms (Bohlen et al. 1970).

An earlier section of this thesis discussed the potential for diminished vitamin D autosynthesis during the dark winter months in the Arctic. It was proposed that decreased vitamin D production resulted in lowered intestinal capacity to absorb calcium, thus rendering the Eskimo hypocalcemic during this time of year. Attacks of Arctic Hysteria during winter months were considered a manifestation of this alteration in physiological homeostasis. Our studies of serum from individuals with Arctic Hysteria-like behavior, however, failed to indicate gross alterations in serum calcium levels throughout the changing seasons. Bohlen et al. (1970) have recently suggested that the critical factor responsible for central nervous system irritability may not be the lowered level of serum calcium, but perturbations in diurnal rhythms of this cation.

The rationale for this proposition will be discussed in this section. In addition, we were able to investigate one subject (#4) according to the methods used by Bohlen among the Eskimos of Wainwright, Alaska. The results of this investigation will be presented as it potentially relates to the Arctic Hysterias and other mental disorders.

CIRCANNUAL AND CIRCADIAN RHYTHMS

Earlier we proposed that serum calcium levels in the Arctic Eskimos were lowered during the dark months of the year. Our study sought to discover this annual cycling of serum calcium, and found that it did not occur as proposed. Bohlen, however, suggested that the circannual rhythm of serum calcium may not be as critical as alterations of circadian rhythms of calcium during the dark period.

Many physiological functions of man vary cyclically according to the twenty-four-hour solar day. Body temperature, blood pressure, pulse, respiration, blood sugar, hemoglobin levels, and amino acids levels change in circadian rhythm. The so-called "stress" or adrenal hormones, concentrations of essential biochemicals, and ions essential to central nervous system functioning also follow a daily pattern. Man also excretes urine according to a daily rhythm as well as to the time of liquid intake. In addition, there are rhythmic fluctuations in the urinary contents, among which is found calcium.

Man maintains physiological stability when his various biological rhythms are in synchrony. Normal functioning seems to depend on the integration of the rhythms into harmonies which enable man to most adaptively rest at certain hours of the cycle, and face stress and high activity at other hours. Maintenance of harmonious biological rhythms depends on several factors. The first includes intrinsic regulatory mechanisms within the physiological system itself which undoubtedly were developed phylogenetically in adaptive response to the twenty-four-hour fluctuations of light in equatorial temperate zones of the world. The remaining factors include external synchronizers, most important of which are light-dark cycles, and social patterns. Under normal circumstances, these external synchronizers also follow a twenty-four-hour cycle. Socially, people follow a daily round of activities, and in most regions of the world these activities are geared to daylight and nighttime. There are, of course, many exceptions, especially in industrial, urban areas, where workers may go on "swing shift," or engage in festivities during the night. These perturbations in daily rhythms are, however, not without consequences, especially regarding mental functioning (Luce 1970)

In the Arctic, light-dark external synchronization from the sun is not possible in summer nor winter. In summer, light is constant; in winter, dark in contrast. Similarly, several authors have noted that social activity patterns likewise follow ill-defined patterns during these periods. In summer it becomes difficult to sleep for long periods. Children are seen playing out of doors at 2 and 3 a.m. Naps are taken sporadically when tiredness ensues. In contrast, the dark winter months are hallmarked by long periods of sleeping, again, however, often without regard to a twenty-four-hour period. The Western world has recently introduced several powerful social synchronizers, the clock, electric lighting, and obligatory schoolwork activities, which perhaps have brought more regularity to the daily routine of the modern Eskimo.

Several authorities who have studied psychosomatic disorders and periodic diseases in man, have recently suggested that symptoms of illness occur when certain rhythms begin to "free-run" out of phase with the twenty-four-hour sleep-activity cycle (Richter, Halberg, and Reimann in Luce 1970:108). Reimann (1963) included intermittent psychosis and epilepsy in a discussion of periodic diseases, and felt that they represented a vulnerability of the central nervous system to irritability and excitation during phases of desynchronization.

Bohlen (1970) investigated several biological rhythms in North Alaskan Eskimos throughout the seasons from 1968-70. He measured urinary excretion, oral temperature, blood pressure, pulse, hand-grip strength, and eye-hand coordination every two hours for ten-day periods in each subject. He found that body temperature and urinary excretion of potassium maintained precise twenty-four-hour rhythms throughout the seasons. Urinary excretion of calcium, however, became "free-running" during the winter months in all Eskimo subjects. Bohlen associated this desynchronization with the increase in apathy, depression, and irritability generally observed among the Eskimo during the winter months.

In addition, he proposed that desynchronization of calcium rhythms potentially imposed even more severe alterations on central nervous system functioning of those individuals already possessing some brain pathology, such as epileptic foci. The Arctic Hysterias and epilepsy were, therefore, regarded as the consequences of desynchronization of the calcium cycle rendering certain predisposed foci in the brain hyperirritable during the dark periods of the year.

To further investigate the relationship of desynchronized circadian rhythms and the Arctic Hysterias, Case #4 was studied according to the procedures developed by Bohlen. The resulting analysis of her rhythms were then compared with two controls which were measured simultaneously, as well as to a large group of normals from the same village who had been studied throughout the seasons during 1968-70.

Methods

The following measurements were performed on Case #4 and two normals from the same village for ten-day periods in January and March 1970. Measures were performed at 0830, 1030, 1230, 1430, 1630, 1830, 2030, and 2230.

(1) Urine was collected by the subject emptying the bladder completely into a graduated

cylinder. Volume was recorded, and a sample was collected in a plastic bottle and frozen immediately.

(2) Oral temperature was measured after the subject had been indoors for over thirty minutes. Thermometer was held in the mouth for at least five minutes.

(3) The subject was asked to count to sixty without being distracted. A watch was stopped when the subject reached sixty and the elapsed time was recorded to the nearest 0.1 second.

(4) Radial pulse was recorded as the number of beats within a sixty-second period.

(5) Blood pressure was determined by pumping the cuff to 160 mm Hg. A stethoscope diaphragm was placed in the anticubital fossa. The valve was released at one heart beat per 2 mm Hg. When the first regular pulse beat was heard, the level was recorded as systolic pressure. When pulse beats ceased to be heard, the level was recorded as diastolic pressure.

(6) Fine motor hand-eye coordination was measured by placing a bowl of thirty-five beads directly in front of the subject. The subject then transferred a bead at a time to a tube on his left. After thirty beads had been placed into the tube, the elapsed time was recorded to the nearest 0.1 second.

(7) Hand strength was recorded with subject assuming a military stance with arms about thirty degrees from the sides of his body. A dynamometer was squeezed as hard as possible with right, then left hand.

These measures were then evaluated at the Chronobiology Laboratories at the University of Minnesota according to statistical procedures developed by Halberg (1969) for analysis of biological rhythms. The analysis was accomplished by the chronobiological spectrum, and the Progressive Least Squares methods.

(1) The chronobiologic spectrum is a visual display and numeric summary of the parameters of a sinusoidal waveform which best fits the original data. In the first row are plotted the original data points over which is superimposed the best-fitting sinusoidal wave. The next six rows are the numeric descriptions of the data and the fitted wave: the start and end time and duration in hours; the mean and SD of the original data; the P value of the fitted wave (all are P .01); and the three rhythm parameters; level (rhythm-adjusted mean), amplitude (one-half peak-to-trough difference), and acrophase ("timing" of rhythm's peak where 360° = period of best fit). In the third and fourth rows are visual displays of the means by which best fitting periods are determined. The amplitude and residual error are plotted for each frequency fitted (28.0-20.6 hours in 0.1 hour decrements). Vertical lines are drawn from the period where amplitude is a maximum and where residual error is a minimum. That period indicated is the one which best fits the data (24.0 hours for oral temperature, urine volume, Na, K, and Cl; 22.6 hours for urinary Ca).

(2) The Progressive Least Squares analysis is a visual display of changes in the parameters of the sinusoidal wave over the entire data span as determined by the least squares analysis of successive overlapping short stretches of data. The data were analyzed in successive 480-hour (twenty-day) intervals, moving one day to the right (a twenty-four-hour increment) for the start of each successive analysis, until the whole span of data had been analyzed. In other words, data from days 0-20 are analyzed and level, amplitude, and acrophase plotted; then the first day is skipped and a new one added, i.e., days 1-21 are analyzed (nineteen days overlapping) and parameters plotted; days 2-22 analyzed, plotted, etc.

Results

Bohlen's data for the general North Alaskan Eskimo population indicated the following: cosinors performed on individual urine electrolytes, referenced to local midnight, demonstrate twenty-four-hour synchronized rhythms for urine potassium at all four seasons. The rest of the urine variables were hit-or-miss by season. However, when cosinors were performed on electrolytes with acrophases referred to the acrophase of urine potassium, all urinary variables had twenty-four-hour periods except calcium. At all seasons calcium was desynchronized (free-running) with all the other variables and with the day. A few variables did not exhibit rhythms at the circadian frequency, but did demonstrate a circannual one, e.g., hand-grip strength, and time estimation.

Analysis of measures performed on Case #4 and controls (010 and 196) indicate the same patterns as the normal population of the village (see Appendix C). There is no feature which distinguishes Case #4 from the controls, or from the normal population of the village. Figure 12 explains the parameters of the best fitting sinusoidal curve at a period of 24.0 hours.

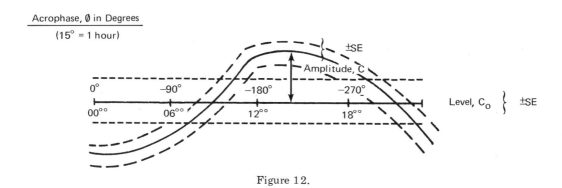

Figure 12.

In summary, it has been demonstrated that the shifting, external, solar synchronizer of biological rhythms has profound effects on the calcium metabolism of the North Alaskan Eskimo. Calcium was desynchronized relative to other electrolytes (sodium, potassium, and chloride) throughout the year. One subject, who manifested Arctic Hysteria-like behavior, also showed the same pattern of calcium desynchrony. Bohlen has suggested that such alterations of calcium metabolism may interfere with the functioning of the central nervous system. In most people this would be manifested by mild anxiety or depression. In individuals predisposed psychologically to anxiety attacks, or in individuals with cerebral pathology, the physiological load is additive, and episodes of the Arctic Hysteria are precipitated. Certain forms of epilepsy could, of course, be manifested as behavior resembling the Arctic Hysterias. These conditions, however, do not depend on abnormalities in calcium metabolism to reveal themselves. On the other hand, perturbations of calcium metabolism may provide the irritative supplement which may trigger the discharge of a cerebral focus. To support this hypothesis, it must be demonstrated that our subjects with Arctic Hysteria-like behavior also manifest evidence of cerebral pathology compatible with a seizure disorder.

X. Arctic Hysteria and Disorders of the Central Nervous System

ARCTIC HYSTERIA is a periodic mental disorder characterized by recurrent, limited episodes of altered consciousness. Often there is memory loss for the event, but otherwise mental abilities are not chronically affected. In previous sections we have investigated the periodicity of solar radiation in the Arctic, its relationship to alterations of calcium metabolism, and the effects of these alterations on the central nervous system. In conclusion, it was suggested that desynchronized calcium rhythms may lower cerebral seizure threshold in those Innuit with irritative foci from other causes, resulting in behavior like the Arctic Hysterias. Disorders of this type are properly classified as epilepsies.

Differentiating hysteria from epilepsy has been a problem in diagnosis for many years. In fact, the similarity and relationship between these hysterias and epilepsy was first described by Charcot at the Salpetriere, where Freud received his first exposures to psychiatric patients. There, in the early 1880s the epileptics and hysterics were placed on a ward separate from the "insane." In this new situation the seizures of the epileptics remained unchanged in frequency and severity. The hysterics, however, were greatly affected by their constant exposure to epileptic patients. Because of their tendency to mimic, they began to simulate every phase of epileptic seizures, the convulsions, the hallucinations, and the bizarre postures (Veith 1965:230). Wallace also recognized the similarity of these conditions and considered epilepsy in his differential diagnosis of Arctic Hysteria among the polar Eskimos of Greenland (Wallace 1960).

Epilepsy is a "state of impaired brain function characterized by a recurrent, periodic, paroxysmal disturbance in mental function with concomitant alterations in behavior or thought processes" (Ervin 1967:796). The manifestations of this type of impaired brain function are varied and depend primarily on which areas of the central nervous system are involved in the seizure activity. Classic grand mal epilepsy includes paroxysms of unconsciousness, tonic and clonic movements, loss of sphincter control, amnesia, and often a bitten tongue or bodily injury from falling. Such seizures reflect a state of generalized cerebral discharge. There are other types of epilepsy which result from more localized impairments or cerebral functioning. The motor areas of the brain are involved, for example, in Jacksonian epilepsy, which may be manifest by progressive, involuntary movements, often without the loss of consciousness. Abnormal electrical discharges originating in or traveling to the temporal lobes result in psychomotor seizures which are manifest by periods of strange, bizarre behavior, or psychic phenomenon. Such patients may be amnesic for the period, or may retain a hazy recollection of the events. Seizures limited to the central, diencephalic areas of the brain are manifest as mere lapses of consciousness, usually without involuntary movements or bizarre psychic events. Amnesia is always present in such forms of epilepsy which are usually referred to as petit mal.

Seizure threshold can be lowered in many individuals prone to epileptic attacks by a variety of environmental and psychic stimuli. Lowering blood sugar or calcium levels may in fact precipitate seizures in many individuals with no particular proclivities toward epilepsy. In epileptics these altered physiological states exacerbate symptoms. Flickering light patterns have recently been found to be common precipitants of seizures (*Medical World News* 1971:17). Anxiety with accompanying hyperventilation can also bring on seizure activity, and many individuals who derive some pleasure or secondary gain from their attacks are able to utilize this mechanism in their production.

The central cause for disturbances of cerebral electrical physiology resulting in epilepsy is varied and in some cases idiopathic. Differential diagnostic procedure, however, includes skull X-ray series, blood serology, fasting blood sugar and calcium, physical and neurological examination, and electroencephalogram (EEG). These procedures were applied to the ten subjects who manifested Arctic Hysteria-like behavior during our fieldwork among the North Alaskan Eskimo in 1969-70. This section of the thesis will discuss the methods and results of this diagnostic inquiry.

Physical and neurological examinations were performed in most cases in the home village of the individual afflicted with Arctic Hysteria-like behavior. Laboratory investigations, X-rays, electroencephalogram, and other diagnostic procedures were performed at various medical facilities serving the North Alaskan Eskimo. (For an explanation of the procedures of physical examination and laboratory studies, see Appendix E.) They included the US Public Health Service Hospitals in Barrow and Anchorage; the State Laboratories in Fairbanks, and the Tanana Valley Medical Clinic in Fairbanks.

The ten cases of Innuit who manifested Arctic Hysteria-like behavior will be presented in this section according to standard medical protocol. This investigation is especially focused on those pathological conditions which can result in dysfunction of the central nervous system such as birth injury and trauma, post meningitic or encephalitic damage, cardiovascular abnormalities, hypoglycemia, syphilis, hypertension, intracranial lesions, cerebral electrical dysrhythmias, etc.

CASE #1 — AMOS

Past Medical History: No surgery, no allergies, no medications. Hospitalizations: May 1967 in Barrow because of one of these "spells."

Habits: He eats well, has a good appetite. Smokes about a pack of cigarettes a day. Denies intoxication from alcohol except on two occasions when he was in the Army.

Review of Symptoms

Head: Rarely gets headaches. *Eyes*: Wears glasses for reading and distance. No diplopia. *ENT*: History of otitis, but on loss of hearing, no tinnitus. Without epistaxis. *Mouth*: Teeth in poor condition, he has not seen a dentist for years. *Neck*: No masses or swelling. *Lungs*: Had a chest X-ray in Barrow in May 1968. No history of TB, asthma, cough, hemoptysis. *Heart*: No history of murmurs, no shortness of breath, cyanosis, ankle edema. *GI*: No nausea, vomiting, jaundice, hematemesis, hematochezia, melena, diarrhea or constipation. *GU*: Without hematuria, nocturia, or dysuria. *Neurologic*: No history of grand mal, paralysis, parathesia. Struck on head with ice at age 12.

Physical Examination

General: A well-developed, muscular Eskimo male in no acute distress. Blood pressure 120/80. Pulse 78 and regular. Respirations 18, regular. Oral temperature 98.6. *Head*: Normocephalic. No evidence of trauma. *Eyes*: Extraocular muscles and visual fields intact. Pupils equal, react to light and accommodation. Left conjunctiva slightly pigmented. Fundi: discs sharp. No hemorrhage or exudate. *Ears*: Both tympanic membranes clouded and scarred. Able to hear watch ticking in both ears. *Nose*: Without obstruction. *Mouth*: Dental caries, two front teeth edentulous. Tongue pink, well-papillated. *Throat*: Slightly injected with postnasal drip. No gag reflex. *Neck*: Without thyromegaly. Carotids equal. No venous distention. *Lungs*: Clear to percussion and auscultation. *Heart*: PMI fifth intercostal space from the mid-clavicular line. $A_2 = P_2$. No murmur, rub, or gallop. *Abdomen*: Flat, muscular. No hepatosplenomegaly. No costovertebral angle tenderness. Bowel sounds normal. No hernia. *Genitalia*: Normal uncircumcised penis, both testes descended.

Extremities: Full range of motion without cyanosis, clubbing, or edema. Chvostek's and Trousseau's signs negative. *Neurologic*: Sensory and motor intact and equal bilaterally. Cranial nerves 2 to 12 intact except for a negative gag reflex. Cerebellar functioning intact. Deep tendon reflexes difficult to elicit. No Achilles or patellar reflex elicited perhaps due to anxiety. Wrist +2. Babinski not present.

Laboratory Findings

Urinalysis: pH 6.0, specific gravity 1.010, albumin negative, sugar negative. 0-3 course granular casts, 0-1 hyaline casts, rare cellular casts, few epithelial cells. *Hematology*: White blood cells 6550/cmm, 70 neutrophils, 18 lymphocytes, 10 monocytes, 1 eosinophil, 1 basophil. Hemoglobin 14.6 gms, hematocrit 43%, sedementation rate 14 mm/hr. *Chemistry*: SGOT 36 s-units, calcium 10.0, inorganic phosphorus 3.3. Phosphatase 58 (2.8 s-units). Serology-VDRL negative. Fasting blood sugar 75. Blood sodium 140, potassium 4.9, chloride 112. BUN 21, uric acid 3.8, cholesterol 165, total protein 7.1, albumin 3.7, bilirubin 0.3, LDH, 153. *Skull X-Rays*: AP, Towne and both lateral views of the skull show calcification in petroclinoid ligament as a variant of normal anatomy. Calcified pineal is not visualized. No fractures or other abnormalities are noted. Impression: Normal skull series. *Extremities*: Normal. *EEG*: Awake, drowsy, sleep, and arousal with chloral hydrate 500 mgm orally. *Background*: Initially apprehensive attenuates alpha rhythm which appears at 10 cps with hyperventilation. Bilateral sleep spindles—normalizes alpha and does not activate. Naso-pharyngeal leads show no epileptiform activity in asymmetry. *Impression*: Normal EEG recording.

In summary, review and investigation of physiological systems indicate no pathology which could contribute to this person's attacks of Arctic Hysteria-like behavior. Episodic attacks were controlled with trifluperazine, a major tranquilizer often used successfully in the treatment of schizophrenia.

CASE #2 — AKEK

Past Medical History: This girl's mother had a pneumonectomy and thoracoplasty several years before her birth. TB became inactive following the surgery. No history of maternal VD. Akek and five siblings have long medical histories of tonsilitis, respiratory infections, and chronic, draining, middle ear infections. One brother died at age 1½ with laryngospasm, which is a symptom sometimes seen in tetany.

Review of Symptoms

(Taken from mother; Akek is difficult to examine directly because of shyness and fear) *Head*: Complains of dizziness frequently when upset. *Eyes*: Vision normal. *Ears*: Frequent earaches and drainage. *Lungs*: Has had pneumonia, and convulsed several times during high fevers five years ago. Her "spells" seemed to start shortly after that. *Heart*: No rheumatic fever, or shortness of breath. *GI*: Frequently feels nauseous when upset. No vomiting, diarrhea or constipation. *GU*: Normal. *Neurological*: Febrile convulsions mentioned above. No weakness, paralysis, or incoordination otherwise.

Physical Examination

General: Small, thin, frightened girl, who finds it difficult to cooperate being examined. Mother's presence is reassuring. Blood pressure 100/60. Pulse 100 and regular. Respirations 30, regular. *Head*: Normocephalic; no tenderness in mastoid area, no trauma. *Eyes*: Extraocular movements and visual fluids normal. Pupils are equal and react to light and accommodation. *Ears*: Right drum inflamed, not bulging. Left normal. *Throat*: Inflamed, tonsils covered with white exudate. Lymphadenopathy present bilaterally in the cervical region. Thyroid not palpable. *Respiratory*: Lungs clear. *Heart*: Apex 5th intercostal space. Sounds normal. Rhythm normal. *Abdomen*: Flat, soft, no megaly or masses. No tenderness. Genitourinary pelvic deferred, no costovertebral angle tenderness. *Neurologic*: Gait and strength normal. No incoordination. No tremors. Cranial nerves functioning symmetrically. Deep tendon reflexes and sensory modalities normal. Chvostek's and Trousseau's signs negative.

Laboratory Findings

Urinalysis: pH 7.0, specific gravity 1.010 negative for albumin and sugar. No casts on cells. *Hematology*: White blood cells 9,500, 75 neutrophils, 18 lymphs, 5 monos, 1 eosenophil. Red blood cells. Hemoglobin 14.2 gms, hematocrit 40%. *Chemistry*: Fasting blood sugar 102, BUN 12. Calcium 10.0, inorganic phosphorus 4.4, alkaline phosphatase 176, uric acid 4.0, cholesterol 180, total protein 7.8, albumin 4.7, bilirubin 0.10, LDH 136, SGOT 44. Lumbar puncture reveals normal pressure, sugar 6.0, protein 32, colloidal gold 1112110000. Serology VDRL nonreactive. *Skull X-Ray*: Skull and chest films normal. Extremities normal. *EEG*: Recordings reveal mitten-spike and wave 3 cps pattern of deep diencephalic origin. Compatible with petit mal episodes.

In summary, this girl exhibits an electrical abnormality in the central portion of the brain which may account for her psychic "spells." The origin of this abnormality may be congenital, or may be based on pathology resulting from high fever or meningoencephalitic infection following respiratory-otitic infection five years ago. Her attacks were controlled with phenobarbital, an anticonvulsant agent.

CASE #3 — KAJAT

Past Medical History: No surgery, no allergies. Had active TB in 1955 and has been on Isoniazid since then. Isoniazid when taken in excess can in itself cause severe psychic symptoms (see *Physicians' Desk Reference* 1971). No other hospitalizations.

Habits: Smokes one pack of cigarettes per day. No alcohol used.

Review of Symptoms

Head: Gets no headaches. *Eyes*: Vision very poor, corrected ten years ago with glasses. No diplopia. *Hearing*: Poor. Enschronic otitis media as a child. Now gets an occasional earache. *Respiratory*: TBC—no cough, hemoptysis. *Heart*: No shortness of breath, angina, or swollen ankles. *GI*: No nausea, vomiting, diarrhea. Occasional constipation, no bloody stool. *GU*: No history of VD. Fathered eight children. *Neurological*: No history of convulsions, paralysis, or parasthesias; no trauma.

Physical Examination

General: Kajat is stooped and has a slightly shuffling gait. He looks older than his stated age. Blood pressure 150/90. Pulse 90 and regular. Respirations 18 and regular. *Head*: No evidence of trauma. No asymmetries. Normocephalic. *Eyes*: Arcus senilis; pupils constricted but react to light. No papilledema, some areas of A-V constriction. No hemorrhage. Extraocular movements normal. *ENT*: Ears bilateral, scarred tympanic membrane. Unable to hear at normal intensity. Some conduction greater than air. Almost adentuous. Several carious molars present. No ulcers. No adenopathy or enlarged thyroid. Carotids symmetrical. *Lungs*: Excursion limited. Some inspiratory rhonchi. Barrel-chested. No other abnormal sounds. *Heart*: Apex four fingers from costal margin. Regular. Heart sounds normal. No venous distention or peripheral edema.

Abdomen: No adipose. Flat, no tenderness or masses. *Genitalia*: Normal uncircumcized male. No scarring. *Extremities*: No unilateral weakness or muscle loss. Chvostek's and Trousseau's signs negative. *Neurological*: Cranial nerves are intact. Deep tendon reflexes absent in patellar and Achilles tendons. Biceps normal. Plantar stimulation elicits withdrawal, but no Babinski.

Laboratory Findings

Urinalysis: pH 7. Specific gravity 1.0 negative for albumin and sugar. 0-4 granular casts. *Hematology*: White blood count 5800 cells/cmm, 60 neutrophils, 20 lymphocytes, 5 monocytes, 1 eosenophil. Hemoglobin 12.5 gms. Hematocrit 38%. *Chemistry*: Fasting blood sugar 105. Serology VDRL nonreactive, calcium 9.2, inorganic phosphate 3.6, alkaline phosphatase 110, BUN 19.0, uric acid 4.3, cholesterol 180, total protein 6.6, albumin 2.9, bilirubin 0.1, LDH 274, SGOT 27. *X-Rays*: AP, Towne and lateral views show calcification of petroclinoid ligament. Pineal is calcified and midline. No fractures or other abnormalities. Normal skull series. Extremities normal. *EEG*: Recording awake and with hyperventilation revealed normal tracing.

In summary, this man demonstrated no pathology grossly affecting the functioning of his central nervous system. Overingestion of Isoniazid in an attempt to suicide following his wife's leaving the village is a possibility to be considered in accounting for his attack, although it is impossible to demonstrate at this time.

CASE #4 — MATAMUK

Past Medical History: Para VI, Gravida X, no surgery, no allergies.
Habits: Does not smoke or drink.

Review of Symptoms

Head: Complains of frequent dizziness and headaches, especially in the evening. *Eyes*: Vision on the left is poor. *Ears*: Often hears roaring and whistling; wonders what it is. *Nose and Throat*: Frequent colds since childhood. *Respiratory*: TB in 1955; inactive, treated with INH. *Heart*: No shortness of breath, rheumatic fever, or edema. *GI*: Occasionally feels great nausea, but no vomiting, diarrhea, or constipation. *GU*: No history of VD, hematurea. *Neurological*: Complains of periodic numbness of lateral right thigh. No weakness.

Physical Examination

General: Rather heavyset, short Eskimo female. Blood pressure 104/70. Pulse 80 regular. Respirations 20 regular. Oral temperature 98.6. *Head*: Normocephalic, no trauma or scarring. *Eyes*: Right 20/20, left 20/200. Extraocular movements normal; pupils equal and react to light and accommodation. Fundi normal. *Nose and Throat*: Dental caries, several front teeth missing. Tongue normal, no adenopathy. Thyroid normal. *Lungs*: Clear to percussion and ausculation. PA. X-ray of chest revealed that the bones and soft tissues of the thorax are normal in appearance. The heart and mediastium are of normal size and configuration. The lungs are clear with no evidence of infiltrates. Calcified hilar nodes are present bilaterally, together with a few small calcified granulomas in both lung fields. The apices of the lungs are clear, as are the costophrenic angles. *Impression*: Old inflammatory disease of the chest. Consider granulomatous origin. The chest is otherwise normal in appearance. *Heart*: PMI 5th intercostal space from midclavicular line. Sounds normal, no murmur. No edema. *Abdomen*: Adipose about 2". No organomegaly, no tenderness. Bowel sounds normal. *Genitalia*: Normal female. No discharges or masses. *Extremities*: Symmetrical. Strength and mass normal. Chvoster's and Trousseau's signs negative. *Neurological*: Cranial nerves function normally. Decreased hearing in left. Bone conduction also decreased in left. Cerebellum function intact. Deep tendon reflexes normal. Babinski not present. Sensory modalities intact.

Laboratory Findings

Urinalysis: Cloudy. pH 5.5, specific gravity 1.023, albumin and sugar negative, numerous mucous threads, 2-3 WBC. *Hematology*: White blood cells 5600, 60 neutrophils, 34 lymphs, 3 monos, 2 eosenophil, 1 basophil. Red blood cells show slight anisocytosis. Hemoglobin 11.9 gms, hematocrit 36%, sedimentation rate 16 mm/hr. *Chemistry*: SGO-T 7 units, alkaline phosphatase 98 (1 unit), calcium 9.8, inorganic phosphate 4.0, fasting blood sugar 90, BUN 14, uric acid 3.8, cholesterol 230, total protein 6.5, albumin 4.3, bilirubin 0-4, serology VDRL nonreactive. Pap smear: Class 1; negative for malignant cells. Shows fair estrogen effect. Blood sodium 144, potassium 4.3, chloride 107. *X-Rays*: The skull is symmetrical. The bone is of normal thickness and density. The sella is of normal size and configuration without evidence of decalcification. The pineal is not calcified. The petrous tips are normal in appearance. *Impression*: Normal skull. Extremities normal. *EEG*: Two-hour recordings showed normal waking and deep sleep record. No activation with hyperventilation or photic stimulation. Drowsiness causes a moderate amplitude mid-left temporal single spike and occasional polyspike which rarely transmits to the right temporal lobe area. Recording is abnormal, compatible with psychometer seizures with deep near midline left temporal focus. *Brain Scan*: Following the intravenous injection of 10 millicuries of Technetium 99 m standard AP scan, PA and both lateral scans of the brain were made. These demonstrate a normal distribution of radioactivity throughout the brain and the surrounding tissues. *Impression*: Normal brain scan.

In summary, this individual demonstrated an abnormal electrica focus in the left temporal area of the brain. Discharges from this focus undoubtedly account for much of her Arctic Hysteria-like behavior. No direct cause for her temporal lobe lesion was found. However, evidence of chronic middle ear infection with hearing loss on the left suggests the possibilty of the brain's being involved in an infectious process sometime in her childhood. Her attacks were controlled with mysoline, an antiepileptic medication.

CASE #5 — KALAGIK

Past Medical History: Maternal history of gonococcal infection treated before Kalagik's birth. Birth uneventful by midwives. Long family history of middle ear disease (see case description).

Review of Symptoms

Head: Frequently "sleepy." Dozes in school, and goes to bed at 6 p.m. No headaches. *Eyes*: Vision normal. *Ears*: Chronic middle ear infections, earaches, and drainage. *Throat and Lungs*: Frequent sore throats, cough, and fever. No TB. *Heart*: No rheumatic fever, no murmurs. *Abdomen*: Frequent nausea and vomiting, often before a "spell." *GU*: No admitted problems. *Neurologic*: Often experiences cramps in fingers, and clenches fist so tight as to be painful. Uses free hand to pry fingers open. Knocked unconscious at age three.

Physical Examination

General: Well-developed young male. Gross coordination is normal. He can run and walk with normal gait. Blood pressure 110/75. Pulse 100 regular. Respirations 20 regular. Afebrile. *Head*: Normocephalic; no trauma. *Eyes*: Vision normal, extraocular movements are normal. Pupils equal and react to light and accommodation. Fundi normal. *Ears*: Both tympanic membranes clouded. No discharge or inflammation now present. *Nose and Throat*: Purulent discharge from nose. Postnasal drip. Inflamed pharynx. Bilateral cervical lymphadenopathy, non-tender and movable. *Lungs*: Clear to percussion and auscaltation. *Heart*: Apex 5th intercostal space, midclavicular line. No megaly, no murmurs. *Abdomen*: Flat, soft, no tenderness. Bowel sounds normal. No masses. *Genitalia*: Normal uncircumcized male. Testes descended. *Extremities*: Well developed, strength good and symmetrical. Chvostek's and Trousseau's signs negative. *Neurologic*: Sensorium was impaired. His performance on a wide variety of tasks shows him to be severely handicapped on a clearly organic basis. His incapacities are so widespread that they have interfered with his learning in all areas. His auditory memory span is very short. He can retain three digits whereas the average eight-year-old can retain five and reverse three or four. He could not grasp the idea of saying digits backwards, let alone hold them in mind long enough to manage it. His hand-eye coordination is so poor that when he tries to copy anything it wanders off the page. Even writing his own name is a hard task for him (see case description). His attempts at assembling picture puzzles and geometric patterns that are easily grasped by most children his age are totally trial-and-error ventures without any grasp of overall configuration of the parts. His incoordination seems to be generalized. There are no involuntary movements or grimaces. His gait is normal. Cranial nerves are functioning symmetrically. Deep tendon reflexes are hyperactive but symmetrical. There is no Babinski. Sensory modalities are normal. Chvostek's and Trousseau's tests negative.

Laboratory Findings

Urinalysis: Urine clear, specific gravity 1.020. Albumin and sugar negative, no cells. *Hematology*: White cells 6500, 75 neutrophils, 15 lymphs, 12 monos, 2 eosenophils, 1 basophil. Hemoglobin 14.5 gms, hematocrit 45%. *Chemistry*: Fasting blood sugar 74, total calcium 7.5, inorganic phosphate 5.8, alkaline phosphate 152 values are compatible with hypoparathyroidism, potassium 4.5. Serology VDRL nonreactive, BUN 13.0, uric acid 4.6, cholesterol 180, total protein 7.8, albumin 4.4, bilirubin 0.1, LDM 200, SGOT 40. *X-Rays*: AP, Towne, and both lateral views show no abnormalities. Extremities normal. *EEG*: First half of recording shows generalized slowing of the dominant frequency and bursts of high voltage show waves positive 6 per second spikes. Anterior and temporal regions show same pattern compatible with a seizure disorder.

In summary, this young Eskimo male displays generalized cerebral electrophysiological disturbances which may account for his Arctic Hysteria-like behavior. Physical examination reveals evidence of generalized brain damage which might account for this seizure disorder as well as his incoordination, slowness to learn, and emotional lability. In addition, his serum calcium is abnormally low, although a previous sample was normal. Reasons for this hypocalcemic finding are presently being investigated and may be related to hypoparathyroidism. There was also evidence of chronic, recurrent, middle ear infection. His attacks were controlled with phenobarbital and dilantin, both anticonvulsive agents.

CASE #6 — SANRAQ

Past Medical History: No surgery, no allergies. No TB. Chronic respiratory and middle ear infections. No drainage from ears.
Habits: Smokes one pack of cigarettes per week. Denies using alcohol and drugs during the period of his Arctic Hysteria-like attack at school.

Review of Symptoms

Head: No headaches, no trauma. *Eyes*: Vision normal. No diplopia. *Ears*: Hearing not impaired, occasional earaches but no drainage. No ringing in the ears. *Nose and Throat*: Frequent colds and sore throats. *Respiratory*: Has had pneumonia on two occasions treated with penicillin. *Heart*: No chest pain, palpitations, or rheumatic fever. *GI*: Appetite good, no weight loss. No cramps, nausea, diarrhea, or constipation. *GU*: Denies intercourse. Otherwise normal. *Extremities*: Strength and coordination good. *Neurologic*: Other than attack of Arctic Hysteria-like behavior, he has never had blackouts or dizzy spells. Denies grand mal.

Physical Examination

General: Very large, muscular, attractive young man. He walks with ease and agility. Blood pressure 120/80, pulse 80 regular. Temperature 98.6 oral. Respirations 18 regular. *Head*: Normocephalic, no evidence of swelling lacerations or old trauma. *Eyes*: Visual fields normal. Extraocular movements normal. Pupils equal and react to light and accommodation. Not constricted. Fundi normal. No papilledema. *Ears*: Hearing grossly normal. External canal clear. Membranes intact. No inflammation or discharge. *Nose and Throat*: Premolar extracted recently, otherwise teeth in good repair. No adenopathy. No inflammation. Thyroid palpable. No masses or enlargement. Carotids palpable and equal. *Respiratory*: Chest clear to percussion and auscultation. No rales. Breath sounds normal. *Cardiovascular*: Pulses equal bilaterally. Apex 5th intercostal space, midclavicular line. Sounds normal. No peripheral edema. *Abdomen*: Flat and soft. No tenderness, no rebound, no masses. *Genitourinary*: Normal male. No costovertebral angel tenderness. *Extremities*: Muscular, equal bilaterally. No wasting. Chvostek's and Trousseau's signs negative. *Neurologic*: Gait and strength normal. No incoordination, no tremors. Cranial nerves 2-12 normal, functioning symmetrically. Deep tendon reflexes and sensory modalities of touch, pain, position sense and vibration normal and equal bilaterally. No Babinski.

Laboratory Findings

Urinalysis: pH 6.8, specific gravity 1.010. No protein or sugar. No casts, blood in cells. *Hematology*: White blood cells 8500. 80 neutrophils, 18 lymphs, 2 monos. Hemoglobin 14.5 gms, hematocrit 42%. *Chemistry*: Fasting blood sugar 85, serology VDRL nonreactive. Calcium 8.8, inorganic phosphorus 5.3, alkaline phosphatase 98, BUN 16.0, uric acid 4.5, cholesterol 174, total protein 6.9, albumin 3.8, bilirubin 0.10, LDN 280, SGOT 90. *X-Rays*: No evidence of fracture or abnormal calcification. Normal films. Extremities normal. *EEG*: Normal two-hour tracing while awake, drowsy, and hyperventilation.

In summary, this sixteen-year-old boy demonstrates no physical pathology which could contribute to his' attack of Arctic Hysteria-like behavior other than borderline low levels of serum calcium and high levels of inorganic phosphate.

CASE #7 — MONTAK

Past Medical History: Gravida 11. Treated for TB in 1960, has been on Isoniazid since. Presently negative sputum and chest X-rays.

Review of Symptoms

Head: No headaches. *Eyes*: Vision mildly impaired, wears glasses for reading. *Ears*: Chronic earaches as a child. None for the past ten years. Hearing is normal. *ENT*: As mentioned above, treated for TB. No shortness of breath, asthma. *Heart*: No rheumatic fever, no known murmurs. No edema. *Abdomen*: Normal appetite. No nausea, vomiting. No diarrhea or constipation. *GU*: Pregnancies uneventful. Menstruation normal and monthly. Denies VD. *Neurologic*: No history of grand mal, no weakness or sensory disturbance. Denies drugs and alcohol.

Physical Examination

General: Very attractive, rather seductive young Eskimo female. Blood pressure 120/80. Pulse 80 regular, respirations 20 regular, oral temperature 98.6. *Head*: Normocephalic, no evidence of old trauma. No tenderness. *Eyes*: Vision compensated by glasses, able to read newspaper. Extraocular movements normal. No nystagmus. Pupils equal and react to light and accommodation. Fundi clear, no papilledema. No hemorrhage on plagues. *Ears*: Drums intact, scarring present. No discharge or inflammation. *Nose and Throat*: No inflammation. No lymphadenopathy. Thyroid normal. No masses. *Lungs*: Clear to percussion and auscultation. No mammary swellings of masses. *Heart*: Apex 5th intercostal space. No murmurs. Regular rhythm. *Abdomen*: Flat, soft, no tenderness. No megaly. Bowel sounds normal. *Extremities*: No wasting or asymmetry. Chvostek's and Trousseau's signs negative. *Neurologic*: Sensorium clear. Sensory and motor intact and equal bilaterally. Cranial nerves 2-12 function normally. No tremors or incoordination. Deep tendon reflexes normal and symmetrical. Babinski not present.

Laboratory Findings

Urinalysis: pH 6.5, specific gravity 1.010 negative albumin and sugar. No cells or casts. Mucous threads. *Hematology*: White blood count 7200/cmm, 72 neutrophils, 16 lymphs, 10 monos, 2 eosenophils. Hemoglobin 13.5 gms, hematocrit 38%. *Chemistry*: Calcium 8.5, fasting blood sugar 75. Serum sodium 142, potassium 4.7, magnesium 0.75. Serology VDRL nonreactive. *X-Rays*: Skull normal, extremities normal. *EEG*: Normal tracing.

Montak demonstrated a severe deficiency of serum magnesium. As pointed out in a previous section, deficiencies of this cation may result in episodes not unlike hypocalcemia (her total calcium was also borderline low) with psychosis, tetany, and peripheral nerve irritability. Intestinal malabsorption, alcoholism, and lack of vegetables in the diet may be factors relatiing to the low levels in this case. Montak is presently being examined medically by the local Public Health Service physician to determine the precise cause of her abnormality.

CASE #8 — SAUTAK

Past Medical History: No surgery, no allergies. No major diseases in family. As a child had pin worms and primary inactive TB.
  Habits: Denies drugs, smoking, or alcohol.

Review of Symptoms

Head: No headaches. *Eyes*: Vision good. *Ears*: History of otitis but no loss of hearing or tinnitus. *ENT*: No bleeding. *Lungs*: No cough, hemoptysis. *Heart*: No history of rheumatic fever or shortness of breath. *GI*: No diarrhea, nausea, hematuresis. *GU*: No pain, no VD. *Neurological*: No history of grand mal, paresis, or paristhesia.

Physical Examination

General: Well-developed young man who looked blankly off into space, and at times would not respond to questioning unless tapped on the shoulder. Blood pressure 120/75. Pulse 80 and regular. Respirations 22, regular. *Head*: Normocephalic, no trauma. *Eyes*: Moved coordinately. No nystamus. Pupils equal and reacted to light and accommodation. No funal hemorrhages, no A-V nicking or papilledema. *Ears*: Normal. *Nose and Throat*: Tongue midline, teeth in good repair, pharynx and tonsils normal. No neck masses or bruits. Thyroid normal. *Lungs*: Clear to percussion and auscultation. *Heart*: No heaves, thrills. Normal peripheral pulses. No venous congestion. Regular rhythm with split first sound heard over precordium. *Abdomen*: Bowel sounds normal. Pain in lower right quadrant which disappeared while examining the patient. No organomegaly, no tenderness. *Genitalia*: Normal male, uncircumcized. No testicular masses. Prostate slightly enlarged. *Neurological*: No abnormalities in gait or coordination but did walk slowly and complained of total body pain. Sensory and motor intact. Cranial nerves 2-12 intact. No cerebellar signs. Deep tendon reflexes normal and symmetrical. Sensory modalities intact.

Laboratory Findings

Urinalysis: pH 6.5, specific gravity 1.02, no albumin or sugar. 0-1 granular casts. Porphobilinogin negative. *Hematology*: White blood cells 4900 with 46 neutrophils, .44 lymphocytes, 2 monocytes, 3 eosenophils. Hematocrit 45%, hemoglobin 15.8 gms. *Chemistry*: BUN 19 mgs%, glucose tolerance test was within normal limits. Stool for ova and parasites was negative. Spinal tap revealed opening pressure of 190 cm closing 150 cm. Fluid clear, 5 RBC per m^3, 2 WBC. Sugar 66 mgs%, total protein 31 mgs%. Serology: blood and spinal fluid VDRL nonreactive. Blood sodium 140, potassium 4.5, chloride 116, calcium 9.8. *X-Rays*: Anterior-posterior, Towne and lateral views of the skull show no abnormal calcifications, displacements, or trauma. Extremities normal. Brain scan normal. *EEG*: Normal tracing.

In summary, there are no physical abnormalities present in examination which would contribute to Sautak's attacks of Arctic Hysteria-like behavior. Episodic attacks were controlled with phenothiazines, which are major tranquilizers often used successfully in the treatment of schizophrenia.

CASE #9 — TESOGAT

Past Medical History: No surgery, no allergies.

Habits: Takes no medication, but does admit to occasional heavy use of alcohol, and has "sniffed" gasoline. Has peculiar eating habits, going on fads for one type of food or another. No weight loss.

Review of Symptoms

Head: Complains of band stretched around his forehead which feels tight. *Eyes*: Vision normal. No diplopia. *Ears*: Chronic middle ear infections until two years ago. Had drainage bilaterally. *Respiratory*: No TB, asthma, or hemoptysis. *Heart*: No rheumatic fever, no shortness of breath, no edema. *GI*: No nausea, vomiting, diarrhea, or constipation. *GU*: No VD, no hematurea. *Neurologic*: No history of grand mal, no trauma, no paralysis or paresthesias.

Physical Examination

General: Very thin, lightly built young man who stares straight ahead with a rather bizarre smile. Blood pressure 115/75. Pulse 80 regular. Respirations 20 regular. Temperature oral 98.6. *Head*: Dolichocephalic, normal in size and proportion. No evidence of trauma. *Eyes*: Vision normal for reading newspaper. Extraocular movements normal, pupils equal and react to light and accommodation. Fundi demonstrate no edema, exudates, or hemorrhage. *Ears*: Membranes milky and scarred. No discharge. Hearing impaired. Bone>air. *Nose and Throat*: No inflammation, teeth in good repair. No adenopathy. No enlarged thyroid. Carotids equal. *Lungs*: Clear to percussion and ausculation. *Heart*: Apex 5th intercostal space, midclavicular line. No murmurs, no edema. *Abdomen*: Unable to relax. Musculature rigid. No rebound; however, and no tenderness. *GU*: Normal male. *Extremities*: Thin, poorly muscled, but symmetrical. No joint limitation. Rows of scratches at each wrist, not penetrating skin. Chvostek's and Trousseau's signs negative. *Neurologic*: Sensory and motor functions intact and symmetrical. Cranial nerves 2-12 are normal bilaterally. No trauma or incoordination. Deep tendon reflexes are active and symmetrical. No Babinski.

Laboratory Findings

Urinalysis: Urine clear, pH 6.0, specific gravity 1.020. No sugar or protein. 0-2 granular casts. No cells. *Hematology*: White blood cells 6000, 70 neutrophils, 20 lymphs, 8 monos, 1 eosenophil,

1 basophil. Hemoglobin 14.5, hematocrit 42%. Red blood cells normal. *Chemistry*: Fasting blood sugar 75, serum sodium 140, potassium 3.7, calcium 9.0. Serology: VDRL nonreactive. *X-Rays*: Skull normal. Extremities normal. *EEG*: Normal two-hour tracing.

Tesogat demonstrates no disorders of the nervous system other than hearing deficiencies which may have played a major psychological role in his attacks. This will be discussed in detail in a later section. His attacks were controlled with phenothiazines, which are major tranquilizers often used successfully in treating schizophrenia.

CASE #10 — NIRIK

Past Medical History: No surgery, no allergies.
Habits: Denies drugs or alcohol.

Review of Symptoms

Head: Dizziness and vertigo when upset. Breathes into a paper bag to "clear head." *Ears*: Colds and middle ear infections during entire childhood, had high fevers often, and drainage from right ear. Often has "ringing in the ears" preceding an attack of hysteria. *Nose and Throat*: Frequent sore throat and tonsilitis, successfully treated with penicillin by U.S. Public Health Service physicans. *Respiratory*: No TB, several episodes of pneumonia treated with antibiotics. *Heart*: No rheumatic fever. No palpitations or corgina. When anxious often feels "shortness of breath." *Abdomen*: Frequently feels nausea and vomiting after she has been approached by a man. Has also experienced periods of voluntary fasting and weight loss. *GU*: Menses normal since age thirteen. No VD. *Neurologic*: Has not convulsed during her attacks. No history of trauma.

Physical Examination

General: Young, very attractive Eskimo woman, dressed in fashionable, Western style, wearing makeup. Hair fashionably arranged. Demonstrates some coyness regarding the examination. Blood pressure 125/85. Pulse 80 regular. Respirations 20 regular. Temperature (oral) 98.6. *Head*: Normocephalic. No evidence of trauma. No tenderness. *Eyes*: Vision normal. Extraocular movements and fields normal. Pupils react to light and accommodation. No papilledema. Fundi clear. *Ears*: Membranes white, shiny. No inflammation. Hearing grossly normal. *Nose and Throat*: No discharge, inflammation, or adenopathy. Thyroid palpable and of normal size and consistency. *Lungs*: Clear to percussion and auscultation. No breast pathology. *Heart*: PMI 5th intercostal space, midclavicular line. No bruits or heaves. Heart sounds normal. No murmurs. *Abdomen*: Flat and soft. No megaly. No mass, no tenderness or rebound. *GU*: Deferred. No costovertebral angle tenderness. *Extremities*: Well-developed, symmetrical. Chvostek's and Trousseau's signs negative. *Neurological*: Gait normal. Cranial nerves 2-12 function symmetrically. Deep tendon reflexes normal bilaterally. Touch, pain, and positive sense not impaired. Toes downgoing with plantar stimulation.

Laboratory Findings

Urinalysis: Urine cloudy. pH 6.8. Specific gravity 1.010. Negative sugar and protein. Many oxalpte crystals. No cells. *Hematology*: White blood cells 5700, 65 neurophils, 20 lymphs, 15 monos. Hemoglobin 13.5 gms, hematocrit 38%. *Chemistry*: Fasting blood sugar 70, serum sodium 140, potassium 4.5, calcium 9.6. Serology: VDRL nonreactive. *X-Rays*: AP, Towne, and lateral views of the skull indicate no fracture, calcification, or other abnormalities. Extremities normal. *EEG*: Normal tracing under awake, drowsy, sleep, and hyperventilation.

In summary, Nirik demonstrated no physical abnormalities which could account for her Arctic Hysteria-like behavior.

SUMMARY OF FINDINGS

The signs and symptoms exhibited by the ten cases, which may be related to their Arctic Hysteria-like behavior, are summarized in Table XVI.

TABLE XVI. SUMMARY OF PHYSICAL FINDINGS

	Case Number									
	1	2	3	4	5	6	7	8	9	10
Birth Trauma or Head Trauma	X	0	0	0	X	0	0	?	X	0
Onset in Childhood	X	X	0	X	X	0	0	X	X	X
Chronic Middle Ear Disease	X	X	X	X	X	X	X	X	X	X
High Fevers	?	X	?	X	X	X	?	X	X	X
Total Serum Calcium 9.0 mg%	0	0	X	X	X	X	X	0	0	0
Low Serum Magnesium	0	—	—	0	X	—	X	0	0	0
Organic Signs on Neurological	0	0	0	0	X	0	0	0	X	0
Cerebral Electrophysiological Abnormalities	0	X	0	X	X	0	0	0	0	0
Attacks Controlled with Anticonvulsant	0	X	0	X	X	0	0	0	0	0
Attacks Controlled with Tranquilizer	X	0	0	0	0	0	0	X	X	X

X = Presence of physical sign
0 = Absence of physical sign

The onset of Arctic Hysteria-like behavior was often in childhood and early adolescence. Recurrent respiratory infection and otitis media were constantly present in the histories of all ten cases. These infections were common among the Eskimo in very early contact times (Fortuine 1968:25, 27, 29), and today constitute a public health problem of considerable magnitude (Brody et al. 1965; Reed et al. 1967; Maynard 1969). Several factors of Eskimo life contribute to the high incidence of respiratory illness and concomitant middle ear disease. Eskimo dwellings are heated with coal, gas, and oil to high, dry air temperatures during the Arctic winter. Protective mucous membrane of the nasopharynx is dried, and vulnerable to infecting organisms. Eskimo dwellings are crowded, and visiting from one household to another is a daily event. Infections are spread rapidly in such social situations. Otorrhea during the first year of life is uncommon in greater United States. In Alaskan natives it is relatively common (Maynard 1969). In addition, as the Caucasian grows older his face grows in a downward direction. Eustachian tubes which drain the middle ear into the pharynx follow this growth, and assume a direction parallel to gravity in the white adult. Middle ear disease is rare, therefore, in the adult Caucasian. Downward facial growth is not as prominent in the mongoloid (see Oshinsky 1964) and eustachian tubes correspondingly maintain a more infantile position perpendicular to the draining assisted by gravity. The middle ear is thus not as easily drained, and, accordingly, is more prone to chronic infection. Otitis media persists from infancy to adulthood in the North Alaskan Eskimo.

Sequelae of these infections most commonly include hearing loss. There is an increased probability of hearing loss with increased frequency of attacks (Maynard 1969). Relative deafness is common among Alaskan natives and may start as early as fours years of age. This disorder may account for a significant degree of scholastic underachievement, apparent inability to learn English, and subsequent difficulties in socializing, and self-image as demonstrated in the history of Case #9, Tesogat. Several of our subjects were examined with the Zenith Audiomiter, 150 1964, Model ZA-110T. All demonstrated severely impaired hearing capacity. Recently Altshuler (1969) has demonstrated that deaf individuals are handicapped in the internalization of rage through sanctions presented verbally, and thus have lowered ability in imposing self-constraints. He found the deaf more prone to acting out anger, and correspondingly less prone to depression.

Chronic otitis media can affect the central nervous system more generally by several other means. These infections are commonly associated with very high fevers in childhood. Infants not infrequently convulse during such febrile periods. Prolonged febrile convulsions has been related to epilepsy later in life (Lennox 1960:394).

The infective organism, commonly haemophilus influenza or streptococcus, may invade the meninges via the bloodstream or by direct extension from the sinuses. This results in a bacterial meningoencephalitis which is fatal in ninety-five percent of the cases. However, with the frequent use of penicillin recently in most villages many of these central nervous system infections can be successfully aborted. The point of their interruption is, of course, a determinant of the morbidity of the sequelae. Gross post-inflammatory damage could result in hydrocephalus, cerebral palsy, and severe mental retardation. Minimal damage could result in epileptic foci, personality disorders prone to hyperactivity and distractableness in childhood and explosive behavior; in later life, minimal incoordination, and mild mental retardation.

It is also conceivable that chronic inflammation of the middle ear may extend through the petrous temporal portion of the skull, and impinge directly on the undersurface of the temporal lobes of the brain, creating scars and irritative foci for abnormal electrophysiological patterns. This condition would be manifest as psychomotor seizures as illustrated by Montak, Case #4.

The frequency of such central nervous system sequelae of otitis media is presently unknown. However, the possibilities clearly merit attention. Scholastic underachievement, lower IQ scores, hyperactivity, personality disorder, pathological intoxication, and epilepsy are problems common to Alaskan natives which might ultimately be attributable to middle ear disease. In our cases of individuals manifesting Arctic Hysteria-like behavior, the relationship is only suggested in retrospect. More definitive evidence could only be afforded by a carefully controlled epidemiological study of hearing loss, otitis, and electroencephalographic abnormalities, with neuropathological specimens confirming the process.

Three of our cases demonstrated direct evidence of electroencephalographic abnormality, the others did not. It should be emphasized that being unable to confirm a diagnosis of epilepsy by EEG is not unusual, even when clinical evidence and therapeutic response are strongly indicative (Noyes and Kolb 1959:270).

XI. The Psychology of the Arctic Hysterias

THE PHYSIOLOGY of the central nervous system is intricately related to mental functioning. The last section investigated some of these relationships from the direction of the pathophysiological effects on mental events. Epilepsy was discovered as an underlying neurophysiological aberration, which in some cases gave rise to Arctic Hysteria-like behavior. Even in epilepsy, however, psychological status may be a major determinant of the course and manifestations of the disorder. Individuals may derive certain gratification or release from their attacks, and may use them in the face of conflict. Attacks can often be precipitated voluntarily by a variety of maneuvers including hyperventilating and observing changing patterns of light. In those individuals who do not use their attacks voluntarily or consciously, unconscious determinants may still be at work. Conflict or shame may generate anxiety which in turn precipitates the seizure by concomitant, involuntary hyperventilation. Furthermore, unconscious conflicts themselves may find some resolution or gratification through the epileptic symptom. The attention one receives during an attack, and the care administered by others afterward, may offer additional secondary gains. The form and pattern of behavior manifest in the attack itself are also largely determined by the motives and psychology of the afflicted individual. This is especially prominent in temporal lobe or psychomotor seizures as illustrated in Matamuk, Case #4. These areas of the brain which are abnormally discharging have been patterned during the socialization processes, and discharge according to these patterns. Artificial stimulation of these areas of the brain during surgery evokes vivid playback of specific past events in life. These areas have, therefore, been referred to as memory centers.

Psychology can be assumed to play an even greater role as a determinant of Arctic Hysteria-like behavior in those cases where physiological aberrations could not be demonstrated. This section will explore various psychological characteristics demonstrated by the ten cases through personal interviews and psychological tests. In addition, some discussion will be devoted to the "basic personality" of the Eskimo with regard to the Arctic Hysterias.

CASE #1 — AMOS

Amos differs strikingly from his peers in demeanor and personality. He prefers to seclude himself most of the time in his room. However, on most occasions when he is approached for conversation, he appears most friendly and eager to talk. Unlike most of his peers, he does not inhibit many of his thoughts and feelings. In fact, on occasion he is almost loquacious. This, by the way, has led many whites who work for the church and government agencies to conclude that Amos is superior in his ability to abstract and to form concepts. Since his school years, teachers and missionaries have instilled in Amos very high expectations for performance and academic achievement.

In many ways, Amos throughout life has considered himself the "chosen one." Initially, Amos, in fact had been chosen by adoption as an infant. His adoptive parents were an elderly couple who were said to have favored and babied Amos most of his life. Amos also grew up with the knowledge that his paternal grandfather and his real father had great "power." Amos personally became indoctrinated with shaman power at the age of seven or eight when he sat almost every evening at the bedside of a granduncle who allegedly had spirit power. Unrepeatable stories were told to Amos at that time. Amos said, "That man taught me a lot about old-fashioned ways. He told me where power comes from; he told me how to get it. Then he died." Shortly after this, at the age of ten, Amos had a supernatural experience which confirmed in his mind his power. His father had sent him on an errand to fill a can with gasoline. The drum was heavy and unmanageable. Amos got to his knees and prayed to God for strength. "Suddenly a spirit entered my body and I felt strong all over. It was a miracle. I could pick up the whole drum over my head and I was only a boy. Ever since that time supernatural things happen to me. When I am alone out in the tundra hunting for caribou sometimes my mind leaves me. I become strong. This has happened two or three times a year since I have been ten years old."

Amos has always considered himself superior to others and has stood aloof from his peers. At about the age of puberty, this became manifested in his feeling "called by God to lead his people in church." Amos attempted to pattern his life after an Eskimo Presbyterian missionary who led the church in his village. In spite of his lack of academic success in school (Amos graduated almost last in his class from high school), the new white missionary and village school teachers felt that he had the intellectual capacity to go through formal academic training requirements to become an ordained minister of the Presbyterian Church. He was, therefore, sent for a year at the university. Amos, in fact, has very poor potential for academic work, and quickly met with failure. He returned to his village, with his hopes and expectations for himself shattered. He steadfastly adhered to the belief in his superior powers and tried to insert himself in church activities at every occasion. People in the community began to consider these attempts as childish and ridiculous and began to gossip about him. He always felt himself rather above putting much effort in the everyday work of hunting and maintaining a household. This placed some burden on his relatives and in-laws, who frequently admonished him to act more like a man not stay at home like a woman. This ridicule and gossip served to enhance his tendency to withdraw from his peers, to consider himself superior, and, on occasion, to demonstrate his powers.

In general, people in the village were quite frightened of him and his potential to do harm. On several occasions, Amos was formally ostracized by village members who phoned for a constable's help from a large village nearby. The constable came and escorted Amos to a psychiatric institute.

Amos, however, knew no way of life outside his village and kept returning. One might speculate that in times past Amos' power may have been accepted and confirmed by his fellow villagers. Today, his academic inabilities to achieve formal missionary status in the church are a painful demonstration of his personal inadequacies and lack of power. Because of this, he is not accepted as a church leader; whereas in times past, he may very well have been accepted as a powerful shaman. This poses an obvious dilemma to the observer in delineating the sources of Amos' psychological difficulties. Is Amos' sense of superiority and grandiosity since childhood years in itself psychopathological? Seemingly, in times past, Amos may have experienced no incongruence between the way he saw himself and the way others saw him. In today's society, however, there is no room for a shaman.

Psychological testing was done on Amos at the University of Alaska and the profiles of the Minnesota Multiphasic Personality Inventory were analyzed (see Appendix F). His profiles indicated superficial friendliness; however, fear of close emotional involvement with others, and a tendency to keep psychological distance between himself and others. They indicated his sensitivity to environmental demands and his avoidance of any situation where his performance would not be considered better than the performance of others. There was also indication that under stress he has the tendency to lose control and act out in "circumscribed" paranoid episodes.

CASE # 2 -- AKEK

Akek is a very small, very shy, but pretty little Eskimo girl who, unlike many of her peers, is extremely frightened of white people. She prefers never to be seen. She stands behind doors and behind the taller members of her peer group when in the vicinity of an elder or a white person. She was very frightened about talking to me and had to be accompanied on several occasions by a girlfriend and on other occasions by her mother. After many conjoint visits of this sort, she would come to see me alone, but even on these occasions preferred to draw in silence rather than talk. The designs usually included objects from her daily life such as dogs, snow mobiles, her house, and Christmas objects. A few of these drawings are included in Appendix C.

Under every circumstance of observation in school, on individual visits, in her home with her peers, and outside in the village, Akek always remained retiring, passive, inactive, always in the background at the end of the line behind others. She would often speak of not having things like snow-goes, which other families could easily afford. She indicated in many ways that with so many children in the family, her parents just did not have the time or the energy available to give her the things, the emotional support, or the interest which Akek felt that she needed. She admitted occasionally losing control of bladder at night while sleeping, and sometimes in the classroom. This would bring the attention and the ridicule of others who teased her for being "a big baby." Loss of bladder control has existed sporadically since she was trained at age two. This symptom may be related to periodic seizure episodes, or they may be symptomatic of her general state of anxiety and the need for mothering.

On a number of social occasions in the village which were attended by all, Akek was observed to be in a state of great panic. When others approached her for conversation, or for a joke, she would often hide her head and burst into tears. On several occasions, she fled from the room and went home by herself. During initial visits with me, she would often tear and blush at the most neutral of inquiries. This behavior was quite unlike the behavior of her classmates who are characteristically almost over gregarious in visiting my office and living quarters, seemingly unabashedly making comments and jokes about the way of the white doctor.

Akek's mother and father have both had a rather hard life. Their economic condition is very poor. Father has a difficult time hunting enough meat to feed his large family. Four children have died in early childhood from respiratory infections, which has added further anxiety and grief about making a living. Akek's parents are very serious, unemotive, unjoyous people who, like Akek, have withdrawn from most of village society because of feeling inferior and ashamed about their lack of achievement in others' eyes.

Akek's seizures have gained her the care and special attention of a white missionary and a Bureau of Indian Affairs teacher who have taken a special interest in "praying that Jesus will take away her affliction." Akek's relation with her siblings is much the same as with her peers. She is scapegoated because she is shy, passive, and retiring. She is easily made the brunt of many jokes and is pushed around by the older, more aggressive children. She is frequently hurt, and cries.

Akek has felt rather neglected and inadequately provided for by parents who have endured many hardships themselves. Furthermore, she is frequently ashamed, put upon, pushed around, and bullied by siblings and peers. This further substantiates basic feelings of inferiority and inadequacy. When confronted by older people whom she considers overwhelmingly powerful and adequate, especially white people, her own smallness, insignificance, and ineptitudes are further emphasized. She withdraws for fear that her weaknesses will be exposed, that she will be asked a question she cannot answer, that the white doctor will find her wanting, and that others will find her stupid. Inwardly she resents being pushed around, yet she can do little to stop this cycle of events. Her seizures afford her some care, concern, and attention she would otherwise not receive, and to a certain extent, give her a supernatural or religious countenance, since many of the religious Eskimos and white people pray to Jesus for the removal of this symptom. The symptom also affords her an escape from the anxiety and conflict-ridden situation of the classroom. While in a "lapsed state" she is beyond the torments and mockery of others.

CASE # 3 — KAJAT

Kajat looks much older than fifty-two. He is a short, muscular, not obese man, with a withered, weather-beaten, dark brown face. He wears traditional style clothing made by his wife. The entrance to his house is filled with Eider duck, caribou meat, and hides. Inside, skin clothing hangs from the walls to dry. He is usually sitting at a small table eating dried meat with an ulu. Kajat is a rather stoic, pensive, outwardly unemotional man, who is fond of talking about past hunts and whaling trips and about the old days when "the reindeer herders made lots of money in the village." He and his brother have grown up and have grown old in this village and are generally considered the patriarchs of the group. These men know the old folk tales and the old dances, and during community celebrations such as Nalakatuk (whaling festival) and Christmas (formerly the Messenger Feast), these men are looked to by everyone to lead in the chanting and dancing. He told me stories of religious experiences his brothers have had during which they have seen "little men and little Jesus on the tundra." He remembers the days "when people had power" (shaman), but will not speak about those times because "we are Christians." At the time of my visits with Kajat, he seemed to be very content and satisfied with his life.

There was no evidence of anxiety or depression. His stream of consciousness was normal. He was oriented to time, place, and person. His memory for remote, recent, and immediate recall of events was within normal limits. Other than his hysterical episode, he has not experienced hallucinations. However, he stated, "My brothers have." Concerning the events surrounding his hysterical attack, Kajat says:

> I didn't know what was happening; I thought she would die. They took her away from me. I wonder what they were doing. They were going to cut her up. Maybe she would be better. Maybe she would die. What would happen to me an old man. My children are gone (five children have married and moved from the village). Nobody would take care of me. I prayed so hard to God. I prayed and prayed night and day, then I guess I got the spirit.

This refers to the belief that if one goes to God with prayer, that he might be filled with the Holy Spirit, during which time one's mind is not one's own.

Kajat had known his wife since boyhood. They had gone together and married for forty some years. She was the only family he had left. He depended on her complimentarily in maintaining his traditional life style. Without her, this would have been impossible. For Kajat, maintaining his life style was maintaining life itself. Without it, he might as well be dead. The threat of his wife's death was a threat to his very existence.

CASE # 4 — MATAMUK

Matamuk is a very amiable, mild woman who indicates great concern about her spells and wants to find out about their cause. She is perplexed that "My brothers know more about my life than I do." Her lapses of memory and sometimes spells of physical violence have interfered with her life since childhood. Matamuk says that when she was about ten years old her spells began. People told her that sometimes her eyes would be open and she would stare straight ahead. She did not seem to see anything. This happened several times at church where she would "enter a trance and would have to be carried home as no one could arouse her from it." "She never knew anything for about an hour then she'd be cross for a while." Matamuk states that she had to repeat the seventh grade because she had missed about half of a year at school during the year 1947-48. She does not remember much of that year, but siblings and friends often used to mention events of that time which she cannot remember. Her father told her that this was not one continuous unconsciousness, but she would awaken for a while and then be out again for about seven months. Because of her spells, she could not continue in high school and returned home after about a year and a half.

Matamuk is above average in intelligence. However, because of her spells she is incapacitated in attempting to adjust to the normal life of an Eskimo woman in this small village. Relatives and villagers recognize her limitations, and thus she is offered only the simplest, most menial roles in the community and church undertakings. She is seldom teased or ridiculed any more; instead, most of the people shake their heads and exclaim, "Can nothing be done for her? Is she hopeless?" Since the age of nineteen, Matamuk has had an intense relationship with the man whom she finally married several years ago. The marriage had been prevented for a long time due to her husband's mother's opposition. Old hostilities existed between Matamuk's and her husband's families. In addition, Matamuk's mother-in-law opposed the marriage on the ground that she felt

Matamuk was incapable of being a wife and mother to her son. After eleven pregnancies and five live births, Matamuk's future in-law's gave in and she was married. It is interesting to note that all five children born were female. Her husband had wished through the years for a male child. Finally, a year following their marriage she gave birth to her first son. Matamuk does not demonstrate any overt guilt about her pregnancies, nor is there any indication that she did not want these children. She denies any intent to harm her male child and maintains this denial with a dispassionate conviction, indicating that her act of trying to eat the child may have been committed without any feeling of guilt that she had done wrong. Indeed in her normal condition Matamuk is a very pleasant, friendly, physically relaxed woman who does not manifest undue anxiety or underlying anger at her husband or children. While she is in a "spell," however, these individuals are often recipients of violent rage.

One would assume that if there were hostile, destructive impulses under tenacious control, and of such intensity as to account for violent attacks on a child and her husband, there would be either evidences of this in fantasy material or evidence of the psychic strain required to keep these impulses in repression. Neither of these seems to be the case, nor is there any extraordinary guilt about the past or apprehension about the future. Minnesota Multiphasic Personality Inventory scores, in fact, reveal no psychopathological tendencies in this woman (see Appendix F).

CASE # 5 — KALAGIK

Kalagik is a plump, well-developed, nine-year-old Eskimo boy. His clothing is tattered, but traditional in style, his parka having been handed down from other siblings. His hygiene is very poor; his hair matted, unbrushed, which is in sharp contrast to most of his peer group. His nose runs constantly down his lip. He is quite frightened and shy and his knowledge of English is limited. When seen by me he usually comes with a friend. Kalagik is not an overly anxious or apprehensive boy. He is for the most part cooperative and friendly with me. His mental content is centered primarily on getting a snow mobile so that he can race around the village with the others. He envies the teenage boys who are able to drive their own machines. He is aware of the fact that he "blacks out," and that people laugh at him for this and other "mistakes." His memory span for immediate recall is very short; he can only remember three digits, while others in his group can easily handle five. He is distractable, and although passive in temperament, is constantly turning from one object to another and appears, therefore, to be slightly hyperactive. His fine motor coordination and eye-hand coordination as revealed in design and copy in art work are grossly impaired as illustrated in a previous section, and strongly indicate minimal brain damage. Almost all of his symptoms can be accounted for on this basis.

These disabling symptoms are a considerable handicap in the school situation. He has great difficulty learning and, because of his distractability and slight hyperactivity, he is a management problem for the teachers. His deficiencies are apparent to his peers who often tease him by calling him "retarded"; and at times, mimic his seizures in play. Kalagik's response on the surface at least seems to be indifferent. He looks on without expression or comment. He is, however, unable to share the mirth of the others.

CASE # 6 — SANRAQ

Sanraq is a large, well-developed, good looking, young Eskimo man dressed in Western style with white shirt and tie. He is very neat and well-groomed and relates in an open friendly manner. On the surface he does not seem to be overly shy or retiring. In fact, he has a certain glibness in his conversation. At the time of my first interview with him, one month had elapsed since the attack of Arctic Hysteria-like behavior. He was seen in his home village. At that time he demonstrated no disturbance of affect. He was not depressed nor was he overly elated. His stream of mental activity was normal and he demonstrated no psychomotor retardation or agitation. His mental content consisted of relating the events surrounding his hysterical episode and his present-day situation in the village. Unlike many of his peers, this young man has had no experience sexually with women.

He states that he is shy with girls and hesitates to speak with them or approach them for fear that he will be turned down. He feels rather unsure of himself as a man. Much of this feeling of inadequacy stems from his being in a transitional position. His family is rather modern by village standards. Thus, he has identified to a large extent with the Western ways. He, therefore, is not acquainted with the finer skills involved in hunting, whaling, trapping, and living the traditional Eskimo life. He has not sought his own identity in traditional ways, and is naturally quite unskilled. The older people in the village do not mock him for this; however, they "wonder what is to become of him." Like many of his peers, Sanraq has dreamed of going to the big city to get a job, to make money, to buy a car, to own a home with running water and electricity, to go to restaurants, to go to movies, to get along with Western ways. His first experience in a Westernized town came when he left his village for a boarding school. In actuality, he was ill-prepared for life in the city. On the one hand, he felt intense loneliness for the visits of his relatives and friends back home; on the other, he found his peers from the city "too fast with booze and women." He was frightened by the city and by his new boarding school situation, which has created even more conflict in his mind. He did not know whether he wanted the village or the Western ways which he had planned for so many years. He felt inadequate in facing either one of these alternatives. His level of self-confidence, in his feeling about himself as a man, sunk to a very low level which further reinforced his reluctance to get dates as so many of his friends in boarding school were doing. He was thus exposed to many jokes and much ridicule about his sexual shyness. To protect himself, he took a rather moral position. Although he is not in actuality very religious, he told himself and others that drinking and women were "not the way to live," and that one should work hard if one were at school. Soon, however, rumors began to circulate that several of the teachers at the boarding school had been drinking and had had a sexual affair. This made it even more difficult for him to maintain this position, since he had admired and looked to these white teachers for direction.

In the midst of "this identity crisis," he sustained an abscessed tooth, and for the first time in his life, had to face the painful procedure of an extraction. He was outwardly stoic about the whole procedure. Inwardly, however, he was terrified. He felt there was no one, or no way he could reveal his frightened state of mind. Several others boys, however, recognized his apprehension and began making remarks about his being "a small town baby. Can't take pain, can't take women, can't take booze." Sanraq states that he was furious inside with his dormitory mates who chided him, with his teachers who did not set a good example for the way people should live, "and with the whole situation of being away from home in a strange city." He stated:

It was just too much for me. I guess I lost control. I can't remember what happened. I guess I was pretty mad. I was okay later though, but I just couldn't concentrate on school. I couldn't think about anything but my home. I don't know what is going to happen now. I don't know. I don't know what I'll do. I don't know what is going to happen to me. Maybe in a little while I will go back to the city. Maybe I will get a job and make some money, buy a car. I don't want to stay here, there is nothing to do. It's boring.

CASE # 7 — MONTAK

Montak is a very attractive, slim Eskimo woman who is dressed rather fashionably Western and speaks English fluently without an accent. Montak was born and raised in this village. Her father hunted, trapped, and went whaling for a living. He maintained a very strict mode of living for his children. All of them, however, were attracted to Western life styles. Montak's brothers and sisters have married and now live in Western cities, some of them with white spouses. Montak, however, was not able to leave her parents. She felt attracted to the city and visited her siblings on a number of occasions but always returned to the village.

After her father's death ten years ago, Montak lived with her mother. During this time, she took a trip to the city to visit her sister. There she met a Western man, he followed her to her village and proposed marriage. He had been raised in the city and had no skills at hunting, trapping, or whaling; nor was he inclined to improve his abilities in these areas. He was an outsider and wished to return to the city with Montak. Montak, however, was torn. She did not want to leave her mother alone in the village. At the same time, she wanted her husband. He compromised and decided to stay in the village with Montak, and managed as best as he could. Three years ago Montak's mother became ill and died. Montak took the death very hard and has "been in mourning ever since." Even now, in speaking about her mother she becomes tearful. Since her mother died, Montak has felt rather cut off from most village activities. Although she is a member of the church, she is not asked to participate in any of the social events, presumably because she is too Western in her living and has married an outsider. In spite of this, Montak is still reluctant to leave the village. She says:

> This is my home. This is where I grew up. This is where my parents lived, and their parents before them, and their parents before them. I can't leave the ghost of my mother and father here. The city is not the place for me, but this village isn't the place for me either. I just can't fit in. I don't know what is going to happen. I miss my mother so. Sometimes I sit and think about her so much that she actually seems to come to me. She would always help me when I felt so bad. My husband doesn't understand. He is not from this village. He can't help me when I get like this. All he thinks about is work. [She states] Sometimes there is nothing for me to do. There is no place for me to go, not here, not to the city. All I can do maybe is die. Then I will be with my mother. My sister tried to commit suicide in the city too. I was there when she did it. She is okay though.

Montak seems to be anxious and quite depressed. While her mother was alive she felt some continuity with fellow villagers; now she feels in limbo. She is unable to make an acceptable life in either the village or the city. She demonstrates no thought disorder, no looseness of associations, no delusions, and no hallucinations other than during the acute hysterical episodes which were outlined in the previous section. She is clearly oriented as to time, place, and person. Her memory for past, recent, and immediate recall is within normal limits. Her ability to concentrate, to calculate, and to abstract are all normal.

CASE # 8 — SAUTAK

Sautak is a well-developed but rather bizarre appearing eighteen-year-old Eskimo man. He avoids eye contact, preferring to stare off into space. He denies, however, that he is hallucinating. He is responsive and cooperative to questions; however, his answers are given rather dispassionately. Other than his rather rigid facade, Sautak displays very little emotion. His face and his body appear to be rather frozen. His stream of consciousness is frequently interrupted by long pauses, during which time he seems quite preoccupied with thoughts other than those which he had been expressing. Blocking is prominent throughout our interviews. He demonstrates no psychomotor retardation, and no real looseness of association. His mental content is centered primarily about feeling "no good, I guess I'm no good. Can't do anything. That is what my father always told me. He would get real mad. He would beat on me. He was like the devil. I couldn't do nothing. He was too strong. I am no good in school. Can't work. People around here always say that Sautak is no good." On many occasions, Sautak became unrealistic and delusional. He maintained that there were people out in space who wanted to kill him. They were shooting at him and hunting him like an animal. "I can't seem to get away from them; they see my every move. They know what I'm doing all the time. They spy on me." He went on to relate that people in the village would spy on him and his family and gossip about them behind their backs. He said, "They think we are always drunk. They think we can't do anything but drink."

Sautak has felt alienated from his family and peers for as long as he can remember. He feels no one has ever understood him or cared for him. He feels that he has only received abuse from his father, his siblings, and peers. He is resentful and angry inside. "When I can't take it anymore, I bust loose. I let everybody have it. Maybe someday I might kill somebody." Sautak never adjusted well in school, and was dropped at the eighth grade. He was not sent on to boarding school as many of his classmates were.

Sautak's sensorium is clear. He is oriented to time, place, and person, and his memory for remote, recent, and immediate recall of events is within normal limits. He feels alienated and cut off from village society. He feels unable to cope and inadequate to the demands of daily living there. He has characteristically handled these feelings by withdrawal, avoidance of tasks, and maintaining an aloof, schizoid position. Villagers do not understand him and gossip about "his bad behavior," and in general feel that he has inherited unfortunate characteristics that run in his family. Sautak's paranoid projection of being spied upon and hunted by people in space is clearly an amplification of his basic feelings of inadequacy in his real life situation in the village.

CASE # 9 — TESOGAT

Tesogat is a very thin, gaunt, slightly disheveled young man who wears a black leather jacket and black cowboy boots. He speaks with a very soft voice. He is unassertive and rather delicate. His affect is generally blunted. There is little evidence of free-floating anxiety, in spite of his expressed fears that he is being watched by others. His stream of mental activity is quite loose. He becomes circumstantial and vague during conversation. There is no pressure of speech, no psychomotor acceleration or retardation. He exhibits ideas of reference, believing that people in his presence turn their heads to talk about him, blow smoke in his face on purpose, and make certain movements with their feet as an indication that he has done something ridiculous. He believes that he will not live long, since others know him to be "no good. Even God knows I'm no good. Maybe somebody will kill me." He admits to occasionally hearing a condemning male voice, accusing him of being weak and womanly. This is an interesting symptom since this young man suffers from a hearing loss in both ears. However, he is able to compensate fairly well by reading lips. He watches others carefully for social feedback. Since early days in school, Tesogat remembers being chided and teased by other children because he was "retarded." He has apparently always been rather withdrawn and did not associate with other children in play.

He is oriented to time, place, and person. His memory for remote, past, recent, and immediate recall is within normal limits. He is able to calculate and concentrate on serial 7's adequately. He demonstrates an inability to abstract and gives concrete responses to proverbs.

In summary, Tesogat has lived a withdrawn schizoid existence through most of his childhood years. This was amplified by his having a hearing loss and being chided and ostracized by classmates, who considered him "retarded." His orientation has also been toward watching others and having others watch him. This particular psychological orientation reaches unrealistic proportions in his delusion of being persecuted by God. He is also actively hallucinating voices.

CASE # 10 — NIRIK

Nirik is a very attractive young woman, dressed in Western style with facial makeup. She speaks English without accent. In spite of her professed shyness with me, she relates rather freely and openly to me during our visits together. She is extremely sensitive and intelligent and is able to articulate the way she feels very clearly. She has a slightly anxious affect, yet during the times that I met with her, this was not overwhelming. Her stream of mental activity is normal, she does not demonstrate blocking or loose associations, nor has she any psychomotor accelerations or retardation. She is preoccupied with sexual themes. Her productions almost exclusively involve this subject. She relates that as a girl growing up in her uncle's home she frequently witnessed drunken quarrels and fights. She stated her uncle often came home drunk and "would do all kinds of things." She implied on this and other occasions that her uncle had frequently behaved sexually in her presence, exposing himself and having intercourse with his wife, and grabbing for Nirik during her years as a very young girl. She stated that she felt like a "stepchild." "He was always taking advantage of me. He was always making me do work. He used me."

Her own parents were nomadic hunters, and had left her to be raised by her uncle because of the burden she would have placed on them and their hunting activities. They did, however, return to the village and reclaim her when she was thirteen years old. She had not seen them for many years and, in fact, responded to them as though they were strangers. She says, "I never really felt part of uncle's family; they left me there and only wanted me for one thing" (again a sexual implication). One afternoon shortly after she had been reunited with her parents, she decided to take a nap. She was awakened to find her father lying next to her completely undressed rubbing her breast. She states, "I was groggy and drowsy for awhile and I didn't realize what was happening, then it frightened me. He was too old. I didn't want him and I ran away." Since that time her father has continued to make suggestions and gestures of a sexual nature toward her which "make me run away."

Nirik graduated with good grades from high school and now works in a local government agency. She is an avid reader of novels and has an extremely perceptive, quick mind. Her goals are to go on for university study. Yet she feels incapacitated by overwhelming anxiety when she appears in public. She relates this to "shyness with boys." She had apparently been quite seductive with many of the young men in the village, and several years ago had been raped by two boys at the same time. She was again raped last year. She is adamant that the boys forced her into it. She states that she is frightened of even holding a boy's hand or speaking to a boy and states, "Isn't that childish. It is so embarrassing to even talk about it." Elders and peers in the village joke and tease her about her shyness with boys. She knows they are very concerned about whether she will ever get married or not. She states, "Right now I can't stand men. I can't stand the idea of being married to one, having to take advantage of me all the time." When she is approached by a man apparently for the most casual conversation she becomes filled with anxiety. If they press their advances too much she gets panicky, hyperventilates, and becomes on occasion quite wild. Basically she deeply resents being used, first by her uncle, then by her father, then several other males of her acquaintance. On the other hand, she wants to be taken care of and loved, and ultimately in her society this is accomplished through marriage. She feels strongly that people in the village do not understand her, nor can they appreciate her. She has set her goals on leaving the village and entering the university.

Nirik is oriented to time, place, and person. Her memory for remote, recent, and immediate recall are within normal limits. Her ability to calculate, concentrate, and abstract are all quite normal.

In summary, Nirik is a young woman who has been abused and sexually traumatized from early life on. She has a strong need to be cared for and loved, and goes about obtaining it through the only medium she has learned, that is, her seductiveness. On the other hand, because of past sexual experiences, she is fearful of men's approaches. She is thus in a conflicting position. She wants love, yet she does not want the sexual contact that accompanies it. Others in the village find her attitude ridiculous and childish. She thus feels misunderstood and cut off from elders and peers.

SUMMARY OF FINDINGS

There are many differences among our ten subjects. They vary greatly in age. Both sexes are represented. Some have demonstrable, underlying cerebral impairments. A few sustained their attacks at the real or threatened loss of a loved one. Others demonstrated psychopathology which transcended their seemingly isolated attacks of Arctic Hysteria-like behavior. All of them, however, were threatened or were actually unable to maintain a way of life that was gratifying socially. Case #3 (Kajat) faced the possibility of having to give up a traditional way of life he had known for so long by the removal and near fatal illness of his wife. Case #1 (Amos) unsuccessfully sought an identity as a religious leader; in doing so he failed to follow the ways of the village hunters and whalers and was considered a "woman." Case #8 (Sautak) withdrew into himself and likewise was not considered a participating, external member of the community. Case #9 (Tesogat) withdrew to an equal degree from the mainstream of his society, perhaps because of the liabilities of hearing loss. Case #7 (Montak) and Case #6 (Sanraq) were attracted to modern Western ways, yet could not feel wholly comfortable away from their village. They fit into neither way of life. Case #10 (Nirik) could not behave as a normal Eskimo girl because of her fear of sexual contact. Case #2 (Akek), Case #4 (Matamuk), and Case #5 (Kalagik) could not maintain a normal Eskimo way of life because of organic difficulties. All of these individuals at some point experienced the anxiety of being inadequate and helpless in maintaining a way of life that others in their village would find acceptable and admirable. They were insecure as to their identity and place in their society. They felt their inadequacies intensely, and feared others would also see their weaknesses. They were shameful at not being able to live up to a "meaningful" way of life. The gossip, ridicule, and joking that followed many of these individuals from childhood on could do nothing but reinforce these shameful feelings. None had the feeling he had sinned or had transgressed. There was nothing to be guilty about even for Case #4 (Montak), who had tried to eat her baby. Instead, all felt impaired, weak, or inadequate, and were ashamed of their "lack of manliness," or their being "different," or not "fitting in." They felt inadequate in their own eyes, and in the eyes of others. Many constantly feared being seen and exposed by others. They wished for escape, somewhere to hide, from themselves and others.

Recently Vallee (1968:566) has emphasized the role of "incongruence" between what an individual is and what he aspires to be as a factor producing psychological stress. He found an exceptionally high rate of emotional breakdown among Innuit women of traditionalistic background who married men from Western, urban backgrounds. These women were enmeshed in two differing, often conflicting, subsystems, as was our example of Case #7 (Montak).

Chance (1965) demonstrated the association between mental illness and incongruence on Barter Island. He showed that these Innuit who identified with the Western culture were likely to be emotionally stable if they had the opportunity to interact intensively with white people. The most unstable, on the other hand, were those Innuit who identified with Western culture, but did not have the opportunities of interacting socially or occupationally with whites as with our Case #6 (Sanraq).

Clairmont (1963) investigated the relationships between behavioral disorders and the lack of opportunity to achieve the goals and culture of the majority group in Aklavik, Canada. These studies have stressed the role of discontinuities between Eskimo culture and the newly adapted Western culture in creating incongruence. This thesis illustrates, on the other hand, that cultural discontinuities are not the only circumstances which generate this painful lack of personal identity. Central nervous system aberrations which create lapses in consciousness, incoordination, and mental subnormalities make "fitting in" a most difficult achievement for many Eskimos. Hearing loss contributes to these difficulties for a majority of Eskimo youth. Separation from a supporting parent or spouse may also render one vulnerable in Eskimo society.

Incongruence, in the sense that we are using it here, refers to the individual not being able to achieve or adapt a way of life which the majority of his group consider proper and worthwhile. We are not referring to an incongruence between the personality of an individual and the "basic personality" of his group, although such a situation potentially could make adjusting to the norms of one's culture more difficult. Furthermore, we suggest that incongruence generates feelings of inferiority, psychological weakness, ineptitude, and shame. In such a state one fears exposing himself to others. In Eskimo society this fear is amplified by mockery and ridicule which are common responses to an individual's mistakes or idiosyncracies. The developing Eskimo youth is "in the eyes of his society" from the time he is a toddler. Toilet training is not learned and controlled privately. Instead, one is joked about, again and again, before an audience of laughing adults until proper control of bowels and bladder are acquired. The Eskimo is sensitive about being seen; being caught at a mistake. His inner self is, for the most part, kept hidden from the analysis of others. Eskimos are said to be permissive in child rearing practices. This usually means that Eskimos rarely admonish a child in anger; rarely lay down explicit sanctions for the child to follow. Verbal instruction is virtually nonexistent. The unsure neophyte must try to interpret and copy as best as he can the behavior of those around him "who know." The modality through which social learning takes place is visual not auditory. There are no prohibitions to violate, no sins to commit, no guilt to experience for a transgression. In traditional Eskimo society there were few prohibitions, and no sins, only mistakes, inabilities, weakness, and silliness. This moral-psychological state to this day is a puzzle to the religious missionary whose theology is based on the concept of sin.

Erikson (1963:251) has pointed out that where shame is predominantly used for social control, individual autonomy and sense of self are retarded. One depends on others in his group to constantly define proper behavior. Such definition from others is in this case an affirmation of

TABLE XVII. POSSIBLE RELATIONSHIPS EXISTING BETWEEN POPULATION SIZE
AND PSYCHOLOGICAL ORIENTATION

General psychological profile seen in	Response to separation from relatives	Degree of autonomy from group	Goal Orientation	Result of inability to achieve goal	Pathological results of chronic inachievement
Small, traditional populations (<500)	Maximal	Minimal	Look to others for affirmation of self	Shame	Paranoid suspiciousness, running away, suicide and dissociative hysterical states
Larger villages and towns (>1000)	Moderate	Moderate	Listen to and follow rules in leading a good life	Guilt	Depression and suicide
Urban societies	Minimal	Maximal	Decide life's course for self	Disappointment	Anomie

one's being and worth. Without this constant reaffirmation from friends and relatives one essentially loses himself. The Eskimo often reacts to threatened separation with the despair of "What will become of me now; what will I do?" When the behavior or comments of the group do not reaffirm one's worth, but instead challenge it through ridicule and gossip, psychological separation is accomplished. Looking to others for affirmation here only leads to self-negation. (For a general discussion of shame and guilt cross-culturally, see Lynd 1958; Piers and Singer 1953; Benedict 1946.)

It is probably fair to say that all people look to others in their society for affirmation of their self. In societies where social behavior is learned auditorially through explicit prohibitions and rules, one is able to gain more psychological autonomy from the group. Here one can pattern his life by what he has learned is proper, admirable, right behavior. He may be able to follow this conscience despite what others around him might say. He has internalized the rules, and feels guilt if they are transgressed. The autonomy gained here renders one to a degree less vulnerable to separation or ridicule from the group. Western society stresses individual autonomy to a major extent. During the later socialization years of adolescence one gains a sense of individual identity perhaps differing from what the group considers praiseworthy, perhaps even differing from previously internalized, cherished life's goals (Blos 1962). Autonomy is achieved. One can leave his parents, relatives, and friends with minimal distress.

We have described above a psychological continuum with characteristics which are undoubtedly present in all people; however, their relative proportions vary (see Table XVII). In small, traditional Eskimo societies it was both adaptive and feasible for the developing youth to look to the time-tested ways of surviving in the precarious Arctic environment. For the sake of the group's biological survival, innovation and deviance from the traditional ways could not be accommodated. In our changing, multifaceted, occupationally diversified society, on the other hand, such rigid conformity would clearly be a hindrance. This orientation, however, is not without certain psychological liabilities, as indicated on the preceding table. The responsibility for making choices for one's life in the absence of well established guidelines is in itself a source of stress. Failure to develop a healthy sense of autonomy in our society is frequently manifest in the form of alienation and identity crisis.

This paradigm may have useful cross-cultural and historo-cultural applications, since it suggests that population size may be the critical variable which shapes methods of social control, which in turn determines many characteristics of personality and patterns of mental disorder.

XII. A Synthesis

IN A RECENT MONOGRAPH Margaret Mead (1970) has pointed out that tradition has been the major factor in shaping human behavior in all cultures of the world since the beginning of prehuman societies from Australopithecine times until very recently. The relative influence of tradition can perhaps be measured by the degree to which a culture or way of life changes from one generation to the next. Viewed broadly, change in way of life from Olduvai times to the present has generally accelerated according to a logarithmic curve. For the majority of human history, change in way of life from one generation to the next has been virtually imperceptible. Since the advent of the machine age with its accompanying increases in population and potentials for geographic and social mobility, change from one generation to the next has been to most people painfully evident. In recent years reliance on the old traditional ways of doing things has given way to processes of innovation, which in many instances abruptly break with the past. In this final chapter, I will take some liberty in generalizing broadly. In doing so I would propose that the psychology of the tradition-oriented person differs in many respects from the psychologies of the nineteenth century industrial man and modern man in Western society.

To many the very notion of "culture" involves an assumption of permanence and durability, a superorganic reality which is perpetuated even though individuals who carry culture in their minds die. Culture for the most part has been seen to be more enduring than the individuals who are its carriers. Lowie (1937:3) considered culture as "the sum total of what an individual acquires from his society—those beliefs, customs, artistic norms, food habits, and crafts which come to him not by his own creative activity but as a legacy from the past, conveyed from formal and informal education." To many living in today's world, including Eskimos and other native Americans, as well as the people of our metropolitan areas, traditional solutions to life's choices and problems are no longer as relevant. A degree of autonomy from the past in fact seems to be required in making one's life-way in the world today.

In her study of the conflict of generations, Margaret Mead (1970) contrasted traditional man, industrial man, and modern man in terms of their repositories for models of behavior. She proposed that traditional man learned his life style from the old people in his family and society. Old people had more experience from the past than others and were esteemed for their lore and wisdom. Industrialization created geographic and social mobility of individuals which resulted in breaking with extended family ties and pioneering in new directions of living. Father, mother, and children were no longer connected to old people and to other members of the extended family. Tradition no longer ruled. The father of the nuclear family did. I would not argue that culture's influence on people's lives was lost. Quite the contrary; nineteenth century industrial man also certainly lives within the contexts and constraints of his culture. I am referring here instead to pyschological orientations. Industrial man was a pioneer—the head of his own household— separated geographically and socially from most of his elders (see Erikson 1950; Mead 1970). The repository of knowledge of how to do things no longer securely rested with the consistent consensus of the collective. This pioneer man, because of his own childhood, carried with him many traditional elements, but perhaps for the first time in history assumed full and total responsibility for making choices regarding his own welfare and the welfare of his nuclear family. He was "the head of the household." Growing up in such a nuclear family, of course, presented different kinds of psychological problems for the children. No longer could their anxiety, angers, demands, and needs be diffused to various extended family members. Now all these feelings, by necessity, were centered on father and mother. In addition, because father and mother were the sole repositories of "how to do things," the child's struggle in forming his own way of life became an interpersonal struggle between himself and his parents. The intensity of feeling, both positive and negative, generated by this small family network, is perhaps partly responsible for intensifying conflicts involved in the Oedipus complex (see Mack-Brunswick 1940) with feelings of antagonism and rivalry with father for possession of mother by the male child.

Several authors (Mead 1970; Toffler 1970; Speck 1972) have discussed the emergence of still a newer more tradition-free, future-oriented, psychological orientation which is increasingly becoming characteristic of modern urban man. In this situation, the repository of knowledge used to solve the problems of living comes to be possessed more and more by the younger generations who are in school, and who are generally busy informing themselves about the latest theories in both the academic and social worlds. Here the hierarchical boss-child relationships which existed in the nuclear family situation are leveled out. Toffler points out that even in business organizations and in our educational institutions the hierarchical ordering has been giving way to more horizontal structuring where individuals come together temporarily to solve problems in a task force kind of format. Modern urban man experiences increasing potentials and pressures toward geographic and social mobility. Items of material culture become increasingly disposable offering him the possibilities, as well as the dilemma of having to make constant choices, not only of material objects, but life style and friendships.

In many respects, most modern men are the antithesis of traditional men in psychological orientation. They have greater autonomy and seem to be able to separate from family and friends rather casually with the knowledge that there will always be new friends and social positions perhaps more personally rewarding. Traditional man depends on his kin and small society to acknowledge and define him. He has not learned to easily separate himself from family and friends. When forced to do so he becomes lonely and despairing. Modern man has been conditioned throughout his youth to anticipate rapid changes in fashions, friends, and life style, and to make the choices and adjustments necessary to meet these changes adaptively. Traditional man has learned one way of life based on methods shared by his society through many years. Such methods are relatively immutable. Way-of-life changes little from one generation to the next. Traditional man is not accustomed to making day by day innovations and creative choices in living his life. He relies primarily on prescribed ways and eschews change. When change is thrust upon him, he often reacts defensively and conservatively. The long period of preparation for adult roles necessary in modern urban society has resulted in the frantic, perpetual searching for an identity seen in today's adolescent. Such a period prepares youth to make the constant choices of living demanded by the diversity of roles available in today's complex, multifaceted society. Adolescence among traditional men is not characterized by this prolonged indoctrination into finding one's unique identity. One's personal identity has in most cases been predetermined. The biography of a traditional man could in many cases be written the day of his birth. Adolescence is therefore less tumultuous; but traditional man is likewise less differentiated as a unique individual standing separate from his traditions and his past.

When a way of life becomes conflictual or ungratifying, modern man has the psychological burden to bear. There are no conceivable possibilities for another way of life. I would propose that such situations in extremes generate the psychological possibility of choosing to change his life. Traditional man in such a situation knows only one way of life. If his life becomes unfortunate for one reason or another, it is his psychological dissociation of "hysterical-psychoses" which has been observed in many diverse societies of traditional men (see Opler 1967:133). The Arctic Hysterias are an example of such a phenomenon in the unique contexts of traditional Eskimo societies along the Arctic coasts.

Within this global framework, we will now proceed to outline the unique factors which we have found to be involved in generating the Arctic Hysterias. The fundamental proposition of this study has been that human behavior is multiply determined and that single, linear, causal theories lack comprehensive and predictive value. Kroeber (1948) in evaluating the mutual influences of psychology and anthropology on one another, remarked that anthropologists tend to take human nature for granted and more or less consider personality a constant while regarding culture as the independent variable. Psychologists, on the other hand, assume that culture is a constant and study personality as the variable. In reality, both are variable, mutually interdependent, and altered by a number of other systems such as environment and demography. Some of these systems have been considered in this volume in describing the context of forces which surrounds the occurrence of the Arctic Hysterias of the Eskimos of North Alaska.

THE ARCTIC ENVIRONMENT

Many travelers to the Arctic have commented on the barrenness of the tundra; the bleakness of the flat, snow-covered, monotonous terrain; and the harsh, relentless pounding of the cold wind. They are impressed by the paucity of distinguishing topographical features; by the silence; by the lack of movement; by the unearthly aura of the Arctic. Such observations would indicate that the Eskimos may experience intense sensory deprivation and boredom in such barren country which would easily account for periods of frenzied madness. The matter is quite the contrary, however, through an Eskimo's eyes. He is sensitive and attuned to variations in topographic features, and quickly recognizes soft snow, packed snow, snow over ice, fresh snow, old snow. All these features have personal and adaptive meaning for him. He sees movement and life where the outsider would see none. He is fascinated, for the most part, with the environment and the living things therein, and is constantly exploring its potential for useable resources. We have, however, discovered several environmental factors which potentially adversely affect the functioning of the Eskimo's central nervous system. We have found that the absence of a regular twenty-four-hour alternation of light and dark affects the circadian cycling of calcium metabolism. Calcium is an essential element in the chemical transmission of the neural impulses, and it has been demonstrated that abnormalities in the physiological functioning of calcium are capable of producing a variety of mental disorders including hysteria-like behavior.

The Arctic environment contributes to abnormalities of calcium homeostasis in other ways, too. Early in the fall, days become shorter and shorter, and the zenith of the sun sinks lower and lower in the sky. By December the days involve only several hours of twilight. By January there is complete darkness with only several minutes of red glow on the horizon at noon. Solar ultraviolet radiation is correspondingly decreased during this time of year. This radiation normally induces chemicals in the skin of humans to produce vitamin D, which in turn enhances the absorption of ingested calcium from the intestine. The cold of the Arctic further reduces the Eskimo's chances of exposure to this essential type of radiation. The Eskimo must protect his skin surface from the cold, and dresses so as to cover all parts of his body except his face. Ultraviolet radiation, of course, is incapable of penetrating his clothing. In addition, the Arctic environment places certain constraints on types of flora and fauna from which sources of calcium might be available for the Eskimo diet. Calcium is found primarily in dairy products and in fish. Milk and other dairy products have been unavailable to the Eskimo with the exception of a short-lived experiment with reindeer herding in the 1930s. Fish are available to a number of Eskimo groups, especially in southern Alaska where large rivers empty into the ocean. In North Alaska, natural food resources have not supplied an adequate dietary intake of calcium. We found that this cumulative chain of events resulted in serum levels which fell on the low end of the physiological spectrum. These low levels, plus abnormalities of circadian rhythms of this element, potentiated dysfunction of the Eskimo central nervous system.

The Arctic cold leads still to another chain of events. As air becomes colder its capacity to carry water decreases. If a given volume of cold air is heated without adding water, the humidity will decrease drastically. In times past, when Eskimos lived in semisubterranean sod igloos, moisture was constantly added to the heated air of the interior by the melting and the dripping of the frozen sod walls. Since contact with Western whalers in the nineteenth century, however, the Eskimo has preferred to live in hastily constructed, two-by-four and plywood shacks heated by coal stoves. In these new dwellings, Arctic air is heated but not humidified. This air in turn dries the moist mucous membrane of the nasal passages and respiratory tract, rendering these surfaces vulnerable to infective agents. Respiratory tract infections are extremely common and often lead to the sequelae of high fevers, middle ear disease, and meningitis. These diseases affect the nervous system directly causing damage ranging from slight to severe, and even to death. Such damage can later be manifested as mental retardation, gross neurological impairments, hyperactivity and inattention, inability to control the emotions, hypersensitivity to drugs and alcohol, and various types of epileptic seizures. Middle ear disease, of course, also contributes to hearing deficiencies which in turn give rise to a host of psychological adjustment problems in school and in society. Abnormalities of calcium are in turn capable of precipitating epileptic discharges.

We have discussed the effect of the Arctic environment on the physiology of the Eskimo. Obviously, this environment partially determines many other aspects of Eskimo life as well. As mentioned above, Arctic climate determines floral and faunal forms available to man as food resources. The plant and animal carrying capacity of this environment will in turn determine the number of humans that can be supported within a given area. Population size and population density in itself is a factor in social and psychological functioning. The size of many Arctic sea mammals still requires a special technology and intense cooperative efforts between men who hunt, and between men and their women who utilize the product of the hunt and who make life and future hunts possible. This adaptive, cooperative orientation necessarily dictates a number of psychological prerequisites, such as the repression of anger and competitiveness.

ESKIMO CULTURAL TRADITIONS

The Eskimo way of life has existed with minimal changes over thousands of years in Arctic Alaska. Their adaptation to living in this environment was delicately balanced, with little room for innovation or deviation from the time-tested, traditional Eskimo ways of doing things. The "Eskimo way of life" was prescribed for all members of the society. Children were expected to model their lives after grandparents or, better yet, someone who lived several hundred years previously who was even a "better Eskimo." In Eskimo society, there was not a great variety of diverse roles available to accommodate diverse idiosyncratic personal needs. A man would become a husband/hunter, and a woman, a wife/mother. Several specialty roles could be assumed in addition to the basic roles. One might become a whaling captain, a shaman, or a midwife. Conformity to the expected role in meeting obligations to kin and society was expected of all. Cooperation and "getting along" was valued as the highest human virtue. Such values, however, were not flexible enough to meet the personal needs of each and every member of the society. Some individuals because of constitutional factors or acquired disabilities, such as hearing loss or epilepsy, might sense an incongruence between what was expected of them and what they could actually perform.

Mutual monitoring of each and every individual in the small Eskimo society was both necessary and feasible. This was accomplished by daily rounds of visiting from one household to the next. Deviant behavior was generally considered foolish, weak, or childish, and was accordingly ridiculed or gossiped about. These sanctions commonly began during the second year of an individual's life, increasing in intensity as he became older. Individuals in this situation possess a particular sensitivity to the attitudes and criticisms of others and are easily shamed and humiliated. Eskimo society on the other hand commonly provides for periodic catharsis of these dissatisfactions and angry feelings. Before Christianity, such outlets took place collectively during the Bladder Festival, the Messenger Feast, and at the whaling festivals. These were not only occasions for night-long chanting and expressive dancing, but were also occasions where one could vent himself personally against another through an established traditional ritual, such as a song contest, or a contest of muscular strength and coordination. Such outlets were also provided collectively and individually during times of psychological or social stress through the shaman's seance. The Eskimos generally considered that everyone had a bit of shamanistic power, some having more than others. Power was the basis for being formally initiated into the ancient arts of shamanism. In addition to various devices, skills, and tricks in the shaman's repertoire, he was also an individual who was able to completely "lose his soul." During such a performance, a shaman would appear to lose control of his senses, scream the sounds of animals, dash about quite wildly, and even proceed to convulsions. The cathartic value of such an outburst, whether experienced directly or vicariously, would obviously have considerable emotional value to a people bound by their roles to proper Eskimo behavior, unable to otherwise release frustrations, dissatisfactions, and angry feelings to one another. The behavior manifest by the shaman, by the Eskimo with epilepsy, and by the Eskimo with Arctic Hysteria is often quite similar. Mutual relationships may exist between them. This is not to say that shamans are epileptics, or shamans have Arctic Hysteria, or Arctic Hysteria is epilepsy. Which behavior came first or predominates as a model for the others is, of course, impossible to determine. Each behavior, however, obviously contains many causal elements shared with the others.

VILLAGE DEMOGRAPHY

The animal carrying capacity of the tundra and coastal areas placed certain constraints on the Eskimo population density. Normally, an Eskimo hunter could provide enough food for himself, his wife, and perhaps two to four children. Traditional population also permitted personal, mutual monitoring of one another's behavior. Family size was sometimes controlled by infanticide, or adopting out of excess children. Intense personal bonds between parents and children, and constant monitoring of individual children's behavior, was characteristic of the traditional Eskimo family. Close personal contact and constant monitoring of behavior also occurs within the small Eskimo community itself. Thus the child soon learns that his behavior is of intense concern and interest to others. The growing Eskimo must learn to control his aggressive and competitive feelings even under the most trying circumstances lest he be considered an inadequate, foolish person. There are few ways the Eskimo can express such feelings when they are generated, for his life is never private. In such small communities hysterical dissociation during a shaman's seance, "speaking in tongues," or in Arctic Hysteria offer the only outlets. We have found that hysterical neurosis is a phenomenon of the small North Alaskan Eskimo villages (< 500). Eskimos in larger villages and in predominantly urban areas demonstrate different patterns of mental disorder manifested in depression and alcoholism.

ESKIMO PSYCHOBIOLOGY

A history of severe, chronic otitis media characterized the subjects presented in this paper. In fact, this disease is extremely prevalent in all Eskimos living in predominantly native villages. It is a disease which begins at age six months and may last into adult life. The children experience repeated episodes of high fever, upper respiratory infection, earache, draining ears, ultimately leading to scarification of the eardrums and damage to the oscicles of the middle ear, which may severely impede hearing. In addition, the high fevers and bacterial dissemination from the middle ear to the bloodstream occasionally results in central nervous system infections. These infections called bacterial meningoencephalitides are now frequently interrupted with antibiotic therapy. Often, however, an individual is left with residual central nervous system impairments which range from severe spastic cerebral palsy, epilepsy, to minimal cerebral dysfunction. Such dysfunction may affect intelligence, ability to read, and ability to concentrate. Such a person so afflicted may be hyperactive and distractible and unable to learn in the normal classroom situation. In addition, in later life he may demonstrate peculiar sensitivities to intoxicating effects of alcohol. As mentioned previously, epilepsy can be manifested in a variety of ways. Psychomotor epilepsy thought to originate in the temporal lobes of the brain may produce behavior indistinguishable from that ascribed to the Arctic Hysterias. In fact, three of our subjects demonstrated abnormalities in their electroencephalograms indicative of epilepsy.

This chain of events is initiated and perpetuated by a series of factors. Villages are small and contact between people is intense. Visiting from household to household is a daily occurrence. Making a fuss over children and infants is, of course, very commonly observed among the Eskimos.

Thus when a pathogenic organism is introduced into the village, it spreads from one individual to another very quickly. The present-day over-heated, dry, drafty, plywood homes of the Eskimo render mucous membranes vulnerable to new pathogens. Aspects of Eskimo anatomy may further render him a receptive host to chronic upper respiratory infections. Adult Eskimos differ from adult Caucasians in the length of the face. The Eskimo face does not grow as far downward, and away from the base of the skull as does the Caucasian's. Such growth in the Caucasian gradually brings the eustachian tubes, which drain the middle ear into the pharynx, into a vertical position where their drainage is aided by gravity. Eustachian tubes in the Eskimo remain in a relative horizontal position, rendering drainage more difficult thus providing the Eskimo with a proclivity to middle ear disease.

We have already mentioned the effect of abnormalities in calcium metabolism and circadian rhythms of calcium on the central nervous system. It is well known that abnormalities in calcium homeostasis are capable of simulating and potentiating epileptic seizures. In addition, certain emotional factors are capable of acutely altering calcium homeostasis. One which is frequently encountered among subjects with Arctic Hysteria is hyperventilation or overbreathing in states of anxiety and stress. One subject, in fact, learned to control her attacks by breathing into a paper bag thus preventing excessive losses of carbon dioxide from her bloodstream. Overbreathing has the physiological effect of increasing the pH of the blood and binding the free calcium which reduces availability for neuronal functioning.

A number of psychological factors were also characteristic of our subjects. The small tradition-oriented Eskimo society strongly sanctions prescribed ways of life for the growing child, and commonly exercises social control through the processes of ridicule, gossip, and shame. The majority of our subjects experienced some real difficulty in adjusting well to the roles expected of them by fellow villagers, and correspondingly felt considerable shame in their lives. Each was caught in an untenable psychological position—on the one hand, needing the security and comfort of their home village; and on the other, "not being quite right," and therefore, experiencing considerable gossip. Each had been reared in an environment where proper behavior was primarily learned by observing and copying the behavior of others, and by being constantly monitored by the family and by fellow villagers dropping in for a visit. These people looked to others for an evaluation of themselves. The subtle disapproval often shown them produced a state of almost constant "fear of being seen, fear of being caught." There was a wish to escape from this situation, yet they could not leave the village. An escape was provided through psychological "time out" which is taken during the dissociative attack. The model for such a way to solve problems in times of stress had, of course, been traditionally present in the behavior of the shaman, and more recently in the behavior of church elders who "speak in tongues."

This summary has woven together the many diverse disparate elements which interact in the phenomenon of the Arctic Hysterias. We have demonstrated, however, that these elements do not interact with the same intensity in every case. There were many differences among our ten subjects in terms of which etiological agent acted as the major determinant of the Arctic Hysteria attack. Several subjects had epilepsy; several were diagnosed as schizophrenic; most had low normal serum calcium levels; one had hypomagnesemia and possible alcoholism. These diagnoses in themselves, however, cannot account for the total phenomena of Arctic Hysteria. At best they may play a precipitating role, with the overall form of the attack being shaped within the context of the other multiple forces considered in this study.

REFINING THE SYNTHETIC MODEL

The synthetic approach which we have tried to use in this study does require more formal treatment than we have been able to give our data thus far. We are presently developing mathematical models capable of dealing with the relationships between various interacting systems which would offer more formal approaches to our data (see Appendix G). Such models become increasingly useful as shifts in Eskimo medical care, population size, and orientation to Western society and products increasingly impinge on traditional ways of living. Such changes have already resulted in the emergence of new patterns of social and psychological functioning. For example, we have demonstrated an increasing incidence of mental disorder as population size and Western contact increases. This study has dealt primarily with the factors involved in the Arctic Hysterias as a psychological phenomenon of traditional Eskimo society in North Alaska. The situation of the Eskimo today, however, is changing and we are presently adjusting and refining our approach to accommodate these changes.

In an earlier section we documented recent demographic changes in the Alaskan native population. In 1950 most people lived in small villages with very few living in any large, predominantly native villages. By 1967 the overall native population grew by 44.5% and an entirely different demographic picture emerged. There was an overall growth of 25% in the smaller villages (up to 500), an overall decline of 2% in villages of 500-900, and a virtual population explosion of over 250% increase in villages greater than 900 in size. Many authors, including Jenness (1968), Hippler (1968), and Bloom (1972), have singled out improvements in the medical care delivery system as one of the principal factors in increasing nature population. Both family size and village size grew, changing the fundamental social reference groups to which the whole social system and the individual were geared. The interdependencies resulting from sharing resources and cooperative hunting were changed, since neither was appropriate to a new cash economy. The old traditional ways were no longer useful, and many remaining social institutions became anachronistic. For example, welfare payments to elderly people suddenly increased the economic significance of the grandparent in a household. This was in contrast with traditional society where the elderly members had little economic significance. The formalized educational system introduced the values of a whole new culture, with ways often inappropriate to the needs of the native child. The person who made great achievements in the traditional sense was not always the one considered a great achiever in terms of the new values. These culturally and individually disintegrative forces have led to a high incidence of mental health problems, including alcoholism, suicide attempts, and other social maladjustments. They also compounded the effects of many other changes influencing the health of the people. For example, the shift to a cash economy meant that many people did not have the time to hunt and subsist traditionally and

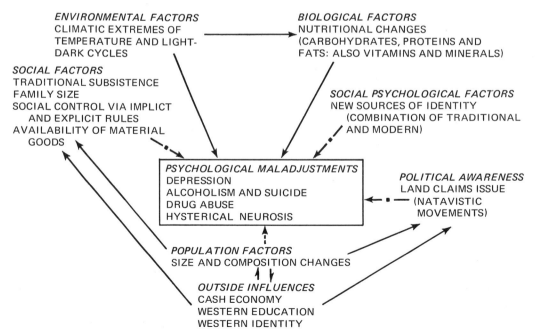

Figure 13. Interactions of recent changes in North Alaska and their possible effects on mental health.

hence were forced to purchase food at high costs. This may have led to important dietary changes which were not traditionally present. For example, there has been a sharp increase in the amounts of carbohydrates in the diet, which are relatively inexpensive to purchase. This may be leading to an increase in the incidence of diseases like diabetes mellitus and extensive dental health problems. Clearly, as population continues to grow without an expansion of local nutritional resources, more food will be imported and the amount of food purchases will continue to increase, and the adequacy of diet may decline significantly.

Figure 13 summarizes the interactions of some of these recent changes in North Alaska.

Alaskan native populations are not the only communities experiencing rapid changes in recent years. The phenomenon is characteristic of virtually every society in the world. In order to predict and deal adequately with the emergent mental health problems facing expanding, ever-changing populations in many areas of the world, we must develop methods which extend traditional epidemiological concepts into a more holistic ecosystems approach, which would include information on a wide range of important social, demographic, biological, and environmental variables. For example, in Alaska we need to account for nonlinear rates of change in economics and population growth, or for the effects of native political movements and associated increases in sense of social identity and their relationships to mental health. The methods we are developing include not only those directly relevant to mental health factors, but also those related to other social, biological, environmental, and demographic factors that may provide important predictions of health status in general.

The intention of this study has been to demonstrate such an approach toward investigating human behavior, in this case, the Arctic Hysterias. This approach sought to provide a wider perspective in understanding behavior by studying man in his total ecological contexts. In concluding, we are forced to observe that man's behavior is shaped not only by intrapsychic processes but also by factors extending from the history of his people to the very forces of the cosmos itself. Recognizing these far-ranging determinants of human behavior is not a mere exercise in academics; it may provide us with a tool to face and adapt to the accelerating changes experienced by man today.

Appendix A

Photos of an Eskimo Woman Going Piblokto
during Peary's Expedition in Greenland[1]

"She was the most accomplished singer
. . . There commenced a wonderful performance of mimicry in which every
conceivable cry of local bird and mammal was reproduced . . . "

[1] Reproduced through the courtesy of the American Museum of Natural History.

"She sang or screamed . . . iah-iah-iah-iaha-ha . . . "

"Flat on her back . . . blowing like a porpoise . . . "

Falling into a convulsion

Demonstrating carpo-pedal spasms

"The whole body trembles for an hour
or so . . ."

"Weak, dazed and with eyes blood
shot . . ."

"No one knew exactly what to do with her . . ."

The Photographers

Going Home

Appendix B

Psychiatric Diagnostic Categories

Depression

Depressive reactions are manifest primarily by lowered spirits, reduced self-esteem, self-depreciation, and sleep and appetite disturbance. The reaction is felt to be due to an internal psychological conflict or to an identifiable external event such as the loss of a loved one or a cherished possession (Diagnostic and Statistical Manual 1968). Anxiety and agitation commonly are associated with some cases. In others, fatigue, restricted movement, and slowed thinking predominate. Many depressed people feel essentially inadequate in coping with life, have difficulty in concentrating on solutions to their dilemmas and increasingly depend on others for direction. Their attention is often withdrawn from real life solutions and focused on their bodies. An aching joint, stomach rumblings, a sour taste in the mouth and a host of other somatic events become their preoccupation.

Hysterical Neurosis

This psychiatric condition is characterized by an involuntary psychogenic loss or disorder of function. Symptoms begin and end suddenly in emotionally charged situations and are often symbolic of the underlying conflicts. Often they can be modified by suggestion alone. All cases reported in Alaskan natives during 1968 were of the conversion type; that is, the disordered functioning was primarily expressed as a transient impairment of one of the special senses causing blindness, deafness, anaesthesia, numbness, paralysis, unsteady gait and trembling.

Anxiety Neurosis

Anxiety is the chief characteristic of all neuroses, including those already discussed under the headings of Depression and Hysterical Conversion. Unlike these conditions, however, the individual with an Anxiety Neurosis is acutely aware of being anxious and has not allowed psychological defensive attitudes, such as displacement and conversion, to interfere with his awareness. Thus, the anxiety neuroses are characterized by anxious over-concern extending to panic. These feelings of ill-defined fright may be experienced in situations not frightening in themselves. The disorder must be distinguished from normal apprehension or fear which occurs in what the society commonly considers a realistically dangerous situation (Mental Disorders 1968:39). Such fear does not commonly invade the total functioning of the personality and is commonly clearly defined and well circumscribed in the conscious thoughts of the individual. Anxiety Neurosis, on the other hand, usually cannot be associated to a definite frightening event. Kayak Phobia may be a case in point. The Kayak Anxiety was initially generated in a frightening situation—that of being disoriented in Arctic waters. In many cases methods of coping with this realistic fear were inadequate. The pervading anxiety which then followed was not so much a response to the fear of being lost on Arctic waters, as to the vague, unrealized fear of being an inadequate man, in Eskimo terms a good hunter and provider.

Neurosis—Other

There were several cases of neuroses so unique in symptomatology that they could not be diagnosed according to any available category of the psychiatric nomenclature. Unfortunately, a description of these unique symptoms was not available for analysis. The cases were diagnosed "Other Neurosis" (Mental Disorders 1969:41).

Psychophysiological Disorders

These disorders are characterized by physical symptoms and actual physical pathology that are caused by emotional factors. Usually only one organ system will be affected in an individual, and that system will usually be under autonomic nervous system innervation. The physiological changes in these organ systems are those that occur normally during certain emotional states, but in psychophysiological disorders, these changes are more intense and sustained, ultimately resulting in structural damage. Some authors hold that there is an inverse relationship between prevalence of psychophysiological disorders and Hysterical Neurosis (Ehrstrom 1951; Parker 1962:78). They point out that psychological conflict is expressed in tradition-oriented societies through hysterical mechanisms, in contrast to change-oriented societies where psychophysiological disorders predominate. It is felt that in the smaller, traditional society one must rely on prescribed means of coping passed down through tradition from elder to younger in coping with life's problems. There are few changes and few agonizing new decisions to be made. When conflicts arise, however, there are few ways that it can be expressed through traditional channels. Instead the conflict is often expressed unconsciously.

In changing societies one must rely to a great extent on himself for making choices in life. This responsibility for new decisions in an everchanging environmental and social world is felt to be extremely stressful. One no longer can depend on the old ways or the old people in facing the everyday problems of life, such as whom to marry, where to work, where to live, what religion to follow and so on.

The organ system involved in such disorders is often in itself an indication of the personality configuration of the individual and will thus be coded accordingly: CV = cardiovascular, GI = gastrointestinal, GU = genitourinary, MS = musculoskeletal, no code = unspecified.

Alcoholism

An individual is considered medically an alcoholic if his intake of alcohol is great enough to damage his physical health or his personal and social functioning (Mental Disorders 1968). Alcohol problems occur in any and all types of psychological disorders including depression. Using alcohol rather than assuming some other symptom such as depression is often seen in individuals whose culture has conflicting values regarding the use and place of alcohol (Chafetz 1969:1013). Many natives in Alaska overtly condemn the use of alcohol and at the same time demonstrate an unusual fascination and preoccupation whenever the topic of alcohol is brought up in conversation. Thus, when one drinks, one does so with conflict and guilt. Reportedly such circumstances enhance the potential of the individuals turning to this troubled psychophysical pattern in times of stress or malaise. This disorder represents the commonest psychiatric problem now experienced by the Alaskan native.

With one exception, there were no reported addictions to other drugs during 1969. Many Alaskan natives with alcoholism were admitted to hospitals not affiliated with the U.S. Public Health Service, especially in Nome, Fairbanks, Anchorage and Juneau. These cases were not available for inclusion in this survey.

Extreme Suspiciousness and Paranoia

Individuals who demonstrate a general attitude of unwarranted suspicion, hypersensitivity, rigid thinking, quick jealousy, excessive envy and a tendency to blame others for life's troubles are often severely incapacitated in maintaining satisfactory interpersonal relations. Such attitudes in mentally disordered Alaskan natives are reportedly often directed at non-natives and accompanied by aggressive behavior. The combination of the above personality features is termed the Paranoid Personality Disorder (Mental Disorders 1968). Noteworthy is the predominance of this diagnosis in Southeastern Alaska.

The Schizophrenias

The schizophrenias are a group of disorders whose central psychopathological process is characterized by certain disturbances in thinking, mood, and behavior. Disturbances in thinking lead to marked alterations in concept formation, such that reality as generally defined and perceived by one's society is misinterpreted. Such misinterpretations often take the form of delusions and hallucinations. Concomitant mood changes may include constricted, aloof lack of emotional exchange with fellow humans, or ambivalent, inappropriate emotional outburst. Behavior correspondingly may appear withdrawn, regressive and bizarre to those not able to share in these divergent, private thoughts and feelings. The schizophrenias are subdivided into several diagnostic subcategories, depending on the nature of secondary symptoms which might accompany those primary disturbances mentioned above (Mental Disorders 1968:33). Many authorities consider that the primary features of schizophrenia can be found in a certain individual in any population, no matter what the biological and cultural circumstances might be. These features so interfere with universal human realities, such as self-care, working ability and relation to other individuals, that they would stand out as abnormal in any culture. Secondary symptoms, on the other hand, are considered to be highly determined by cultural contexts of the afflicted individual (Joseph and Murray 1951; Kroeber 1952). They have undergone profound changes in our own society during the last century. Individuals assuming the demeanor and identity of Napoleon Bonaparte are now rarely encountered. Instead, patients complain about being controlled by television waves which is clearly a reflection of prevailing cultural forces in our society. Among the Eskimos of Igloolik, Canada, Teicher (1954) and Carpenter (1953) reported three individuals who believed they were possessed by spirits and behaved so bizarrely that they were hospitalized. The authors concluded that they were schizophrenic and "the hallucinations and delusions, while expressed in terms compatible with Eskimo culture could otherwise readily be duplicated on the wards of any mental hospital" (Teicher 1954:534).

Whatever the case may be, the clinical form assumed by an individual suffering from schizophrenia is undoubtedly to a certain extent a reflection of his society.

Subtypes

Paranoid Schizophrenia. This type of schizophrenia is characterized by the presence of persecutory or grandiose delusions, often associated with auditory hallucinations and excessive religiosity. The individual may behave in a hostile or grandiose manner and might often be observed staring into space or conversing with his "inner" voices.

Undifferentiated Schizophrenia. This condition is distinguished by the acute onset of primary schizophrenic symptoms, often associated with confusion, perplexity, dreamlike dissociation, emotional turmoil and excitement, depression or fear. In many cases the individual recovers within days or weeks, but sometimes the disorganization becomes progressive. Chronic undifferentiated schizophrenia refers to long-lasting, ongoing personality processes of a similar nature to symptoms described above. Acute undifferentiated schizophrenia may eventually crystalize into catatonia, hebephrenia, paranoid or chronic undifferentiated schizophrenia in the minority of cases which become progressive (Mental Disorders 1968:34-35).

Schizophrenia with Unique Secondary Symptoms. There were apparently several cases of schizophrenia so unique in symptomatology that they could not be categorized into any available subtypes and were thus termed "Schizophrenia—Other."

Manic-Depressive Psychosis

These disorders are marked by severe mood swings with a tendency to intermittent periods of remission. During the manic illness an individual may exhibit excessive elation, irritability, talkativeness and accelerated speech and movements (Mental Disorders 1968:36). He will usually not sleep much and keeps himself involved in constant activity. Extreme persisting aggressiveness is sometimes seen. One case was reported in a Yuit Eskimo.

The Epilepsies

Epilepsy is a syndrome characterized by periodic, transient episodes of alterations in the state of consciousness which may be associated with involuntary movements and/or disturbances of feeling or behavior. These symptoms are regarded as manifestations of disturbed electrophysiological activity in the central nervous system. The disturbance is probably neurogenic rather than psychogenic, although psychological factors have been known to often play a major role in precipitating seizures in individuals having a tendency toward them. The actual metabolic derangement which results in an epileptic attack is probably not the same in all patients or even the same at all times in any one patient. In such individuals the equilibrium of the central nervous system seems to be in delicate balance, and a seizure may be precipitated by a minor psychological disturbance, such as that produced by hyperventilation (Noyes and Kolb 1958:268-269).

Appendix C

Drawings by Case #2—Akek and a Female Peer; Drawings by Case #5—Kalagik and a Male Peer; Letter Written by Case #9—Tesogat

Figure C1. Drawn by Case #2—Akek. Note absence of arms, possibly indicates some feelings of helplessness.

Figure C2. Drawn by Case #2—Akek. A female peer.

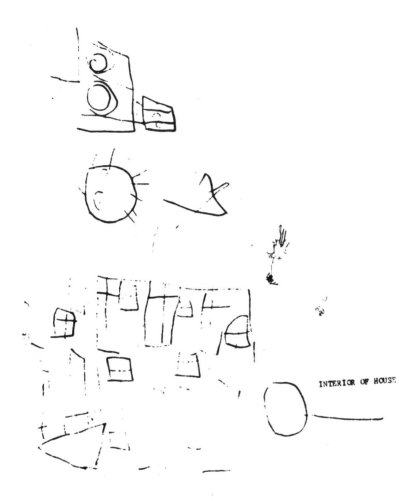

INTERIOR OF HOUSE

Figure C3. Drawn by a female peer of Case #2—Akek. Note close quarters in bed arrangement inside of house.

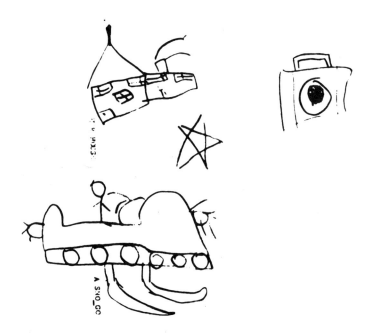

Figure C4. Drawn by Case #2—Akek.

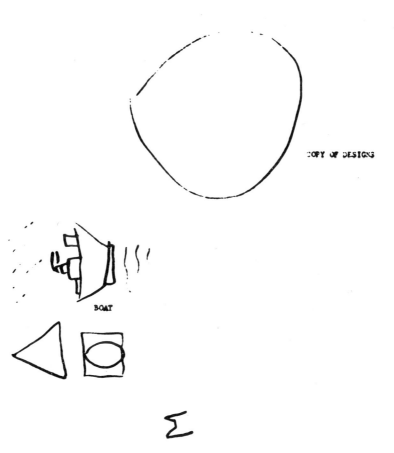

Figure C5. Drawn by Case #2—Akek.

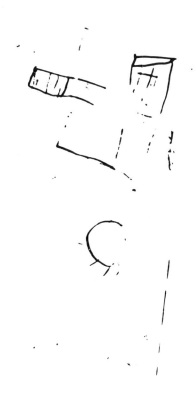

Figure C6. House and sun drawn by a female peer of Case #2—Akek.

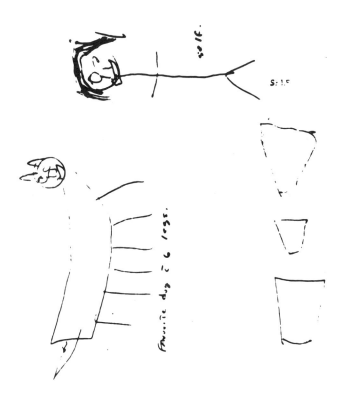

Figure C7. Drawn by Case #5—Kalagik.

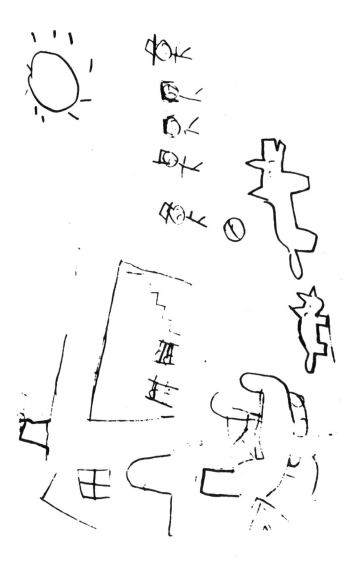

Figure C8. Drawn by a male peer of Case #5—Kalagik.

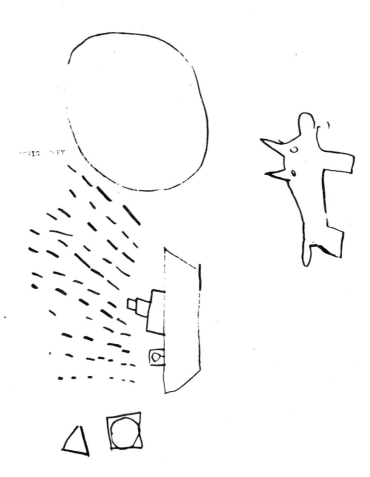

Figure C9. Drawn by a male peer of Case #5—Kalagik.

By writting these words I'm about to write
is it going to hurt me? or is it going to
help me and others that may need help.
Because right now I want to write the
the thoughts I use to have if only
I could remember them. Why is it
I jump to every move - a sudden move
or a sound no matter it be loud or
not. Or is it because I am under
people no matter they be big or small
they may be either in mentle or in
size. Which makes me hurt by jumping
because I am tired of jumping
       Or Could this be hurting other?

Figure C10. Written by Case #9—Tesogat.

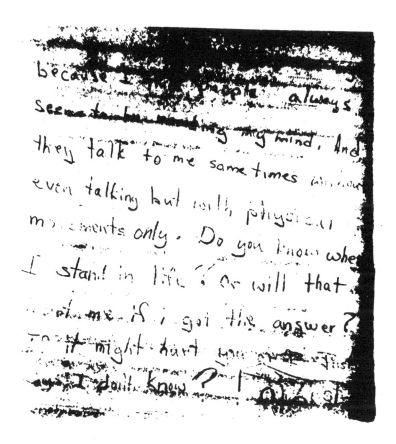

Figure C11. Continuation of letter written by Case #9—Tesogat.

Appendix D

Chronobiological Analysis of Circadian Rhythms in Case #4 (Female), and Two Normal Subjects from the Same Village

When cosinors were performed on electrolytes with acrophases referred to the acrophase of urine potassium, all urinary variables demonstrated 24-hour periodicity except calcium.

A) Time estimation in seconds

Subject # (age)	N obs.	P value (SE/C)	Level, C_0* or $\bar{X}$ ($\pm$SE)	Amplitude, C ($\pm$SE)	Acrophase, ϕ (.95 conf. arc)
Males					
010 ( )	29	>.10 (0.95)**	56.0 ($\pm$1.8)	3.7 ($\pm$3.5)	-57°
196 ( )	30	>.10 (0.52)**	61.0 ($\pm$1.7)	5.6 ($\pm$2.9)	-80°
Female					
( )	27	>.10 (0.81)**	39.8 ($\pm$1.7)	4.0 ($\pm$3.3)	-90°

B) Heart rate in beats per minute

Males					
010 ( )	30	<.01 (0.23)	85 ($\pm$2)	14 ($\pm$3)	-235° ($-217, -252$)
196 ( )	30	>.10 (1.31)**	76 ($\pm$1)	2 ($\pm$2)	-294°
Female					
( )	27	>.10 (0.81)**	68 ($\pm$1)	2 ($\pm$2)	-326°

C) Systolic blood pressure in mm Hg

Males					
010 ( )	30	>.10 (0.73)**	106 ($\pm$1)	2 ($\pm$2)	-317°
196 ( )	29	>.10 (0.84)**	112 ($\pm$2)	3 ($\pm$3)	-37°
Female					
( )	27	>.10 (2.14)**	108 ($\pm$1)	1 ($\pm$2)	-82°

D) Diastolic blood pressure in mm Hg

Males					
010 ( )	30	>.10 (0.47)**	67 ($\pm$1)	3 ($\pm$2)	-340°
196 ( )	29	>.10 (0.93)**	79 ($\pm$1)	2 ($\pm$2)	-49°
Female					
( )	27	>.10 (0.77)**	72 ($\pm$2)	4 ($\pm$3)	-23°

E) Eye-hand coordination in seconds per 30 beads

Males					
010 ( )	30	.04 (0.40)	59.4 ($\pm$0.8)	2.9 ($\pm$1.2)	-110° ($-63, -156$)
196 ( )	30	>.10 (0.51)**	48.6 ($\pm$0.8)	1.8 ($\pm$0.9)	-342°
Female					
( )	27	>.10 (0.47)**	52.2 ($\pm$0.9)	3.9 ($\pm$1.8)	-53°

Subject # (age)	N obs.	P value (SE/C)	Level, C_o* or $\overline{X}$ (±SE)	Amplitude, C (±SE)	Acrophase, ϕ (.95 conf. arc)

F) Oral temperature in degrees Fahrenheit

Males					
010 ( )	30	>.10 (1.49)**	97.3 (±0.1)	0.1 (±0.1)	$-356°$
196 ( )	30	<.01 (0.21)	97.9 (±0.1)	0.5 (±0.1)	$-12°$ (−346, −38)
Female					
( )	27	>.10 (1.27)**	97.8 (±0.1)	0.2 (±0.2)	$-86°$

G) Right hand-grip strength in pounds

Males					
010 ( )	30	>.10 (0.66)**	36 (±1)	2 (±1)	$-326°$
196 ( )	30	>.10 (0.49)**	57 (±2)	6 (±3)	$-293°$
Female					
( )	27	.04 (0.41)	56 (±1)	4 (±2)	$-275°$ (−234, −316)

H) Left hand-grip strength in pounds

Males					
010 ( )	30	<.01 (0.28)	54 (±1)	6 (±2)	$-282°$ (−253, −311)
196 ( )	30	>.10 (0.74)**	66 (±1)	3 (±2)	$-317°$
Female					
( )	27	>.10 (11.6)**	60 (±1)	0.1 (±2)	$-44°$

I) Urine volume in ml/hour

Males					
010 ( )	30	<.01 (0.27)	99.8 (±14.5)	67.9 (±18.4)	$-317°$ (−280, −353)
196 ( )	29	>.10 (0.71)**	54.8 (± 5.8)	12.8 (± 9.0)	$-209°$
Female					
( )	26	.09 (0.43)*	70.5 (±8.6)	24.0 (±10.3)	$-142°$

J) Urine sodium in mEq/hour

Males					
010 ( )	30	>.10 (0.86)**	9.98 (±1.17)	2.25 (±1.94)	$-259°$
196 ( )	29	.07 (0.42)*	10.07 (±1.19)	3.98 (±1.69)	$-205°$ (−159, −250)
Female					
( )	26	.06 (0.40)*	6.76 (±1.11)	3.45 (±1.38)	$-172°$ (−121, −223)

K) Urine potassium in mEq/hour

Males					
010 ( )	30	<.01 (0.23)	2.00 (±0.24)	1.45 (±0.33)	$-203°$ (−178, −229)
196 ( )	29	<.01 (0.14)	2.53 (±0.22)	2.19 (±0.30)	$-188°$ (−172, −205)
Female					
( )	26	.02 (0.33)	2.50 (±0.28)	1.00 (±0.33)	$-153°$ (−109, −198)

L) Urine chloride in mEq/hour

Males					
010 ( )	29	>.10 (0.82)**	4.89 (±0.55)	1.02 (±0.84)	$-23°$
196 ( )	29	>.10 (0.54)**	6.21 (±0.49)	1.39 (±0.75)	$-269°$
Female					
( )	26	>.10 (0.76)**	5.00 (±0.45)	0.94 (±0.72)	$-200°$

M) Urine calcium in mg/hour

Males					
010 ( )	30	<.01 (0.22)	3.04 (±0.30)	2.03 (±0.46)	$-53°$ (−32, −74)
196 ( )	29	>.10 (1.46)**	4.88 (±0.54)	0.62 (±0.90)	$-59°$
Female					
( )	26	>.10 (0.47)**	4.85 (±0.42)	1.23 (±0.58)	$-175°$

Appendix E

Physical Examination and Laboratory Studies

The medical examination of ten Eskimos who manifest Arctic Hysteria-like behavior was performed according to the procedures outlined in *Principles and Methods of Physical Diagnosis* (Hopkins 1965).

Past medical history was obtained by inquiring about previous illnesses, injuries and operations. In addition, each physiological system was reviewed carefully to elucidate the general health of the patient. Such an inquiry may shed light on the present illness, or it may suggest other unrelated diseases or defects that warrant investigation or require medical attention.

Physical examination was then performed on each subject with particular attention to those functions of the body which might be related to disorders of the central nervous system. Normal findings on this examination would include:

General
> Blood Pressure 120/80.
> Pulse 80/min regular.
> Respiration 20/min regular.
> Oral Temperature 98.6° F.

Head
> Normocephalic, or normal size and shape of head.
> No evidence of trauma.

Eyes
> No lesions of conjuctivae (skin of inner lids), sclerae (whites) or irises (colored part of eye). Extraocular muscles are normal when eyes move symmetrically in all directions. Pupils should be equally dilated and constrict when light or an approaching object (accommodation) is presented. Vision is tested in all fields according to quadrants for each eye separately. Fundus is examined with an ophthalmoscope. Cornea, lens and media should be clear. Optic discs and mucula should be free of exudate (swelling or hemorrhage). Retinal vessels should be regular in size and shape without compression in nicking.

Ears
> Hearing is grossly tested by noting the distance from the ear a ticking watch can be heard. External canals should be free of cerumen and discharge. Drums should be intact and give no evidence of infection, perforation or scarring.

Nose
> Should be free of congestion, discharge and tenderness over sinus areas.

Mouth
> Lips, mucosa, gums, teeth, tongue, tonsils and pharynx should all be examined separately for the presence of infection and function.

Neck
> Range of movement is examined. Thyroid gland should not demonstrate enlargement or nodules. Lymph nodes should not be enlarged or tender to palpitation. There should be no venous distention, and carotid pulses should be equal bilaterally.

Lungs

Size, shape, symmetry, equality and degree of expansion should be noted. Respiration should be examined in terms of depth and rate. On percussion all areas of the thorax should demonstrate normal resonance. No dull or flat areas should be found. Breath sounds are examined with a stethoscope. There should be no rales (crackling noises) or friction rubs.

Breasts

Size, contour, symmetry, scars and consistency should be noted. There should be no evidence of masses, tenderness, nipple discharge or skin lesions.

Cardiovascular

The character of cardiac impulse should not reveal abnormal pulsations or retractions, shocks or thrills. The point of maximum impulse is normally in the fifth intercostal space approximately 8 cm. left of the midsternal line. Heart sounds should reveal no abnormal intensity, rhythm, rate or murmur. Peripheral vessels should be symmetrical and pulsate with the heartbeat.

Abdomen

Size, shape and scars should be noted. On palpating the abdomen there should be no involuntary or voluntary rigidity or tenderness. Organs should not be enlarged or demonstrate masses. The presence of herniation in umbilical, femoral and inguinal areas should be looked for. The character of peristaltic sounds is examined with a stethoscope.

Genitalia

Presence of scars, discharge, tenderness or masses is abnormal.

Extremities

Limbs should reveal no deformities, no bowlegs, knock-knees or saber shins. Muscle development should be adequate and symmetrical. Joints should not be swollen or limited in motion. There should be no varicose veins or swelling (edema) in the lower extremities. Calcium deficiency may give rise to tetany with spasmodic involuntary contraction of the hands and feet (carpopedal spasm). Chvostek's sign may also be positive in such cases. This sign is elicited by tapping the cheek along the course of the facial nerve; homolateral contraction of the facial muscles will occur. Trousseau's sign may also be demonstrated in tetany. The wrist and metacarpophalangeal joints are flexed; the interphalangeal joints are extended; the finger tips drawn together and the thumb is pulled into the palm. Compression of the arm, manually or with a blood pressure cuff to decrease blood flow, is needed to elicit this sign.

Neurological

Gait should be steady and strong with normal rate, stride and rhythm of legs and arms. Symmetry of all muscles and movements should be noted. There should be no involuntary tremors, jerks, kicks or writhing. Cranial nerves should be examined separately and should function adequately and symmetrically. Nerve I—smell is tested with coffee grounds or perfume in a small test tube. Nerve II—vision—tested as under examination of the eye. Nerves III, IV and VI are responsible for symmetrical movements and following of the extraocular eye movements. Nerve V is normal when jaw muscles demonstrate adequate and symmetrical function and bulk. Three divisions of Nerve V also supply sensory branches to the face. This is tested bilaterally with light pin prick and cotton touch. Nerve VII is responsible for the facial muscles. Nerve VIII is normal when hearing and balance are intact. Nerves IX and X are tested by examination of the folds of the pharynx and by the normal presence of the gag reflex. Swallowing should be normal. Nerve XI is normal when cleidomastoids and trapezius muscles function to turn the head and shrug the shoulders. The tone is examined for Nerve XII and should extend in the midline, should not have tremor, fasciculation or wasting. Deep tender reflexes are elicited by tapping with a reflex hammer on tendons at the wrist, behind and in front of the elbow (triceps and biceps), at the knee (femoral) and behind the ankle (Achilles). Response should not be asymmetrical, increased or absent. The bottom of the foot is stroked with a blunt object from lateral heel, along lateral side to toes. A Babinski response is abnormal and occurs when the big toe extends and toes fan to such stimulation. Peripheral sensory modalities are tested bilaterally according to nerve distribution. Pain is tested by pin prick; touch with a cotton wisp; position by passive manipulation and questioning; vibration with a tuning fork; and hot and cold sense with test tubes filled with water.

Laboratory studies included examination of the urine (urinalysis), blood (hematology), and serum chemistry. Normal values for these studies include the following:[1]

Urinalysis
    Urine should be clear.
    pH (4.8-7.8).
    Specific Gravity (1.002-1.040)
    Sugar and protein should not be present grossly. There should be no red or white blood cells, no casts or crystals. Bacterial cultures should be negative.
Hematology
    White blood cells—7,200 (4,400-11,600)/mm^3
        neurophils (1,800-7,700) = 59%
        basophils (0-200) = 0.5%
        eosenophils (200-450) = 2.7%
        monocytes (300-800) = 4%
        lymphocytes (1,000-4,800) = 34%
    Red blood cells
        erythrocyte count 4.2-5.4 million/cu mm
        hematocrit = erythrocyte packed volume—42 ml/100 ml
        hemoglobin concentration = 11.5-16.0 gm/100 ml blood
        sedimentation rate—Westergrin method (0-20 mm/hr)
Chemistry
    sodium 325 (312-338)mg%   136-146 m-Eg/ml
    potassium 16. (13-19)mg%   3.5-5.6 m-Eg/ml
    chlorid 369 (337-400)mg%   96-106 m-Eg/ml
    inorganic phosphorus 2.5-4.5 mg% adults
                4.0-   children
    calcium 8.5-10.5 mg% (9.0-11.0 mg% for autoanalyser methods)
    magnesium 2.1 (1.6-2.6) mg%
    blood urea nitrogen (BUN) = 5-20 mg%
    uric acid 2.5-8 mg%
    total protein 6-8 mg%
    albumin 3.5-5.5 mg%
    bilirubin total 0.2-1 mg%
    LDH (lactic dehydrogenase) 90-200 mU/ml (Alaska Psychiatric Institute norms)
    SGOT (serum glutamic oxaloacetic transaminase) 10-50 mU/ml (Alaska Psychiatric Institute norms)
    alkaline phosphatase 30-80 mU/ml (Alaska Psychiatric Institute norms)
    cholesterol 150-280 mg%
    fasting blood glucose 60-110 mg%
    serology—VDRL—should be nonreactive
    lumbar puncture: should be clear, no cells
        pressure 150 (70-180) mm H$_2$O
        sugar 60 mg%
        protein 28 (12-43) mg%
colloidal gold depends on the precipitation and varying degrees of discolorization of a solution of gold chloride by a series of dilutims of cerebrospinal fluid. Certain curves are indicative of pathological processes resulting in abnormality of protein content. For example, 5555554432 may indicate general paresis.
Skull X-ray
    Skull should be symmetrical. Bone should be of normal thickness and density. The sella turcica should show no enlargement or erosion of bone. Pineal may or may not be calcified. If calcified,

can be visualized, and should be in midline. Films of extremities should demonstrate no malformations or osteoporosis.

Electroencephalograph (EEG)

This is a technique of recording through the intact skull the amplified electrical potentials which accompany brain activity. Normally about 10 electrical impulses originate in the brain every second and show characteristic voltage. In epilepsy there may be paroxysmal bursts of abnormal cortical activity affecting both rate and voltage of these currents. Abnormalities in EEG are also observed in many conditions other than epilepsy and tend to assume characteristic patterns. It has been found that about 85% of persons with a history of epilepsy show abnormalities of EEG during a 15-minute recording in the interval between convulsions as compared with 10% of the normal population. When such abnormalities occur they tend to be of the same general type as those observed in the form of seizure (grand mal, petit mal, temporal lobe) from which the patient suffers. A negative report, however, does not rule out the possibility of epilepsy. Abnormal discharges may be so deep in the brain, or occur so infrequently as to be missed during routine recording.

The typical grand mal recording is characterized by rapid development of high voltage (200 u.v.) spikes occuring at a rate of 20-30 per second. Petit mal seizures are characterized by the bilateral synchronous occurrence in all leads of high voltage rounded waves occurring at the rate of 3 per second, usually with a spike superimposed on each round wave. In psychomotor attacks the electroencephalographic tracing shows slow high voltage, square topped waves occurring at the rate of 2-4 per second. Frequently, fast, low-voltage waves are superimposed in the crest of the slow waves (Merritt 1964:769-770). More characteristic of temporal lobe, psychomotor epilepsy is the occurrence of spike discharges from the temporal lobe as evidenced by our Case #4.

NOTE

[1] Unless otherwise specified, values are based on those reported in "Biological Handbook, Blood and Other Body Fluids," D. Dittmer, Ed., Federation of American Societies for Experimental Biology, 1961.

Appendix F

Evaluation of Minnesota Multiphasic Personality Inventory Scores
for Case #1—Amos, and Case #4—Matamuk[1]

Case #1—Amos

(1) Male, age 32
(2) Elevated L scale
(3) Peaks on Scales 4, 6, 9
(4) T = 71, 70, 79, respectively, on above scales

Interpretation: Here, because of the unknown elevation of the L scale score, it is not possible to make any definitive statements about the overall validity of this profile. However, I will assume that the L scale is not so elevated as to invalidate the rest of the profile. However, any comments about L scale elevations as made above for Case #1 still apply here.

The information given here suggests a 946′ profile, although we cannot be certain of this.

Individuals with this code very often are poorly socialized, impulsive individuals, who exhibit a good deal of restlessness, low frustration tolerance, moodiness and irritability. These characteristics often lead to poor adjustment in the areas of work, peer relations and marital adjustment.

While often superficially friendly, individuals with this code are afraid of close emotional involvement with others and keep distance between themselves and others. Persons with this code are often very sensitive to environmental demands and avoid any situation where performance will not be better than that of others. Under stress and especially when drinking (which is common) these individuals tend to lose control and act out. Drinking can also, at times, lead to "circumscribed" paranoid episodes.

Case #4—Matamuk

(1) Female, 32 years old
(2) MMPl Code ′-87 24016
(3) Validity scales within limits except for L = 11

Interpretation: First, there are two rather puzzling aspects to this code. One is that both a (′) and (-) precede the code. This is a redundancy, since a (′) indicates that all scales following are within the "normal" range (below a T score of 70) and a (-) indicates that all scales following are below a T score of 54. Usually the (′) would be omitted if there is no scale evaluation above 54. However, it is possible that the scorer may have just wanted to underline the lack of evaluation of this profile. Second, the space between 7 and 2 is puzzling, since there are usually no spaces left between scale numbers. In general, therefore, I would say that assuming the coding is accurate in spite of these inconsistencies, this would be essentially a normal profile if it were not for the score of 11 on the L scale. This score is just within the unacceptable range (T = 73) and suggests that the respondent tended to put herself in the most favorable possible light by covering up and denying personal faults. Since the items on the L scale are rather obvious, it may sometimes be inferred that a high score here indicates a rather "naive" defensiveness. High L scorers may often come

146

from lower socioeconomic strata, and may be rather unsophisticated about psychological tests. The average L score is 4 ($T = 50$). These factors, as reflected in a high L score, are, of course, probably influencing scores obtained on the clinical scales so that a less pathological profile is obtained.

NOTE

[1] Special gratitude is extended to Jerome Platt, Ph.D., Chief of Experimental Studies Section, Hahnemann Medical College, for his assistance.

Appendix G

Quantitative Ecosystems Approaches[1]

The accompanying table outlines the basic models we are developing to deal with changing patterns of mental health at quantitative levels. The first step involves assembling our data into meaningful equations for purposes of analysis and organization. The second step involves sorting out these variables for significant interrelations and applying statistical techniques to weigh each variable in our model. Several statistical methods are being considered. Multiple interaction programs and factor analysis are useful in sorting out the statistically significant associations among clusters of variables. The application of multiple and stepwise multiple regression analyses can yield the rank order and statistical significance of the associations of each variable in the equation with respect to the particular health problem. The application of a Bayesian regression model in this ecosystems approach can also be used. This method allows for the continuous refinement, description and updating of the states of knowledge on a given problem by continually extending *a priori* distributions and hypotheses with new information. This method, when perfected for computer use, should work well in an ecosystems approach where there is a prior data base and where new data collected may modify prior assumptions or hypotheses concerning the health problem.

The third step is the use of Monte Carlo simulation techniques. These techniques allow data from individuals or subsets of the population to be plugged into the equations in order to

TABLE GI. FORMAL ECOSYSTEMS APPROACH TO CHANGING MENTAL HEALTH PROBLEMS

Step 1.   Establish Basic Models for Health

^{A}Demographic + ^{B}Economic + ^{C}Nutritional + ^{D}Environmental + ^{E}Outside Cultural Influences + ^{F}Biological + ^{G}Sociocultural + ^{R}Remainder = Health Factor(s).

Step 2.   Statistical Methodology
   1.   Multiple interaction programs and factor analysis
   2.   Multiple and stepwise multiple regression analysis
   3.   Bayesian inference theory
   4.   Establish equations for given health variable

Step 3.   Prediction
   1.   Given changes in the distribution of variables using Monte Carlo methods of simulating future health variables

Step 4.   Feedback
   1.   Supply predictors to community leaders and health authorities for future health status and community needs
   2.   Evaluate predictions and evolve further refinements of models

---

determine the outcome in specific cases. Alternative outcomes of the population as a whole can be simulated, for example, by substituting possible expected or hypothetical changes in one of the statistically significant variables such as the changing population size and composition. This technique is constrained by the time span of the data. Nevertheless, it is possible to continuously update and revise the model and increase its predictive accuracy.

The fourth step is to feed back information about individuals and the population as a whole to the proper authorities in health and community areas. Finally, no model showing rapid change can be static. We must continuously feed in new data, test new hypotheses and refine our models further.

In summary, such a formal extension of the ecosystems approach may have important ramifications for mental health in many communities both in and out of the Arctic that are undergoing similar rates of change. From a theoretical point of view, many biological anthropologists are interested in the evolution of man in the 20th century. The Arctic Eskimo is undergoing a very rapid rate of sociological and environmental change, testing the limits of man's adaptability. Because this adaptability is closely tied to man's physical and mental health status, the significance of such an approach gives important clues to the operation of natural selective factors shaping the evolution of this population as it adapts to the stresses of the impinging Western world.

From a practical point of view this approach provides new directions in the prevention and the treatment of mental disorder. If, for example, the following chain of events can be demonstrated (traditional Eskimo visiting patterns in densely populated dwellings, respiratory illness $\longrightarrow$ central nervous system impairments $\longrightarrow$ adverse effects on school performance, tolerance to alcohol and psychological status of a population), prevention programs have many obvious potential points of input.

Second, in the treatment of mental disorders themselves, this approach would help establish those factors in the individual's social and biological environment which reinforce and perpetuate his disorder. Once looked for and identified, factors could be introduced which could interrupt the equilibrium of this cybernetic system.

NOTE

[1] The subject of this section was originally presented at the Preventive Health Program of the Second International Symposium on Circumpolar Health, Oulu, Finland, June 22, 1971, in a paper entitled "An Ecosystems Approach in the Arctic," by S. Katz and E. Foulks.

References

I. A SYNTHETIC APPROACH

Benedict, R.
   1932   Configurations of Culture in North America. American Anthropologist 34:1-27.
Benedict, R.
   1934   Patterns of Culture. New York: Houghton Mifflin.
Billig, O., J. Gillin, and W. Davidson
   1947   Aspects of Personality and Culture in a Guatemalan Community. Journal of Personality
      16:153-187, 326-368.
Kardiner, A., Ed.
   1939   The Individual and His Society. New York: Columbia University Press.
Katz, S., and E. Foulks
   1969   Mineral Metabolism and Behavior: Abnormalities of Calcium Homeostasis. American
      Journal of Physical Anthropology 32:229-304.
Lidz, T.
   1966   Adolf Meyer and American Psychiatry. American Journal of Psychiatry 123(3):330.
Mandelbaum, D.
   1949   Selected Writings of Edward Sapir. Berkeley: University of California Press.
Mead, M.
   1928   Coming of Age in Samoa. New York: Morrow.
   1930   Growing Up in New Guinea. New York: Blue Ribbon.
   1935   Sex and Temperament in Three Primitive Societies. New York: Morrow.
Moore, B., and B. Fine
   1968   A Glossary of Psychoanalytic Terms and Concepts. New York: The American
      Psychoanalytic Association.
   1956-1971   Transcultural Psychiatric Research Review. Montreal, Quebec: McGill University.
Wallace, A. F. C.
   1961   Culture and Personality. New York: Random House.
Whiting, J.
   1961   Socialization Process and Personality. In Psychological Anthropology: Approaches to
      Culture and Personality. F. Hsu, Ed. Homewood, Illinois: Dorsey. pp. 355-380.
   1964   Effects of Climate in Certain Cultural Practices. In Exploration in Cultural
      Anthropology. W. Goodenough, Ed. New York: McGraw Hill. pp. 511-544.
Whiting, J., C. Kluckhohn, and A. Anthony
   1958   The Function of Male Initiation Ceremonies at Puberty. In Readings in Social
      Psychology. E. Macoby, T. Newcomb, and E. Hartley, Eds. New York: Holt. pp. 359-370.

II. PROCEDURE

Freedman, A., and H. Kaplan, Eds.
   1967   Comprehensive Textbook of Psychiatry. Baltimore: Williams and Wilkins.
Noyes, A., and L. Kolb
   1968   Modern Clinical Psychiatry. 7th Edition. Philadelphia: W. B. Saunders.
Szasz, T.
   1970   The Manufacture of Madness. New York: Harper and Row.
Wallace, A. F. C.
   1960   An Interdisciplinary Approach to Mental Disorder Among the Polar Eskimos of
      Northwest Greenland. Anthropologica, N.S. 11(2):1-12.

III. THE ARCTIC HYSTERIAS AND RELATED MENTAL DISORDERS

Aberle, D.
    1952   Arctic Hysteria and Latah in Mongolia. Transactions of New York Academy of Science
        14(7):294-297.
    1968   Alaska Natives and Their Land. U.S. Public Health Service, Federal Field Committee for
        Development Planning in Alaska. Washington, D.C.: U.S. Government Printing Office.
Baahuus-Jessen, J.
    1935   Arctic Nervous Diseases. Veterinary Journal 91:339-350, 379-390.
Balikci, A
    1961   Suicidal Behavior Among the Netsilik Eskimos. North 8(4):12-19.
Bertelsen, A.
    1905   Neuro. Patologiske Medelelser fra Grønland. Bibliotak for Laeger. Kobenhaven
        6:109-135, 280-335.
    1930   Grønlanske Medicensk Stat. of Nosografe. Medelelser om Grønland 140.
Birket-Smith, K.
    1959   The Eskimos. London: Methuen & Co.
Boag, T.
    1966   Mental Health in the North. *In* People of Light and Dark. M. Steensel, Ed. Ottawa,Can-
        ada: Department of Indian Affairs and Northern Division.
Bogoras, W.
    1909   The Chuckchee. Memoirs, American Museum of Natural History 11:42.
Brill, A.
    1913   Pibloktoq or Hysteria Among Peary's Eskimos. Journal of Nervous and Mental Disease
        40:514-520.
Butler, G.
    1965   Incidence of Suicide Among the Ethnic Groups of the Northwest Territories and Yukon
        Territory. Medical Services Journal (Canada) 21:252.
Cranz, D.
    1820   History of Greenland. London: Longman, Nurst, Ries, Olme, and Brown.
Czaplicka, M.
    1914   Aboriginal Siberia: A Study in Social Anthropology. Oxford: Clarendon.
Dall, W.
    1870   Alaska and Its Resources. Boston: Lee & Shepard.
DePoncins, G.
    1941   Kabloona. New York: Reynal & Hitchcock.
Ehrstrom, M.
    1951   Medical Investigations in North Greenland 1948-1949, II. Acta Medica Scandanavia
        140(IV):254-264.
Flinn, D.
    1964   Functional States of Altered Awareness During Flight. Aerospace Medicine 36:537-544.
Freuchen, P.
    1935   Arctic Adventure. New York: Farrar and Rinehart.
Grygier, T.
    1948   Psychiatric Observations in the Arctic. The British Journal of Psychology 39:84-96.
Gussow, Z.
    1960   Pibloktok Hysteria Among the Polar Eskimos. *In* Psychoanalytic Study of Society. W.
        Muensterberger, Ed. New York: International Universities Press.
    1963   A Preliminary Report of Kayak-Angst Among the Eskimo of West Greenland: A Study
        in Sensory Deprivation. International Journal of Social Psychiatry 9:18-26.
Hall, H.
    1918   A Siberian Wilderness: Native Life on the Lower Yanisei. Geographical Review
        5(a):1-21.
Hoebel, A.
    1941   Law Ways of Primitive Eskimos. Journal of Criminal Law and Criminology 31:663-684.
Holm, G.
    1914   Ethnographic Sketch of the Angmagsalik Eskimo. Medelelser om Grønland 29:1-47.
Honigman, J.
    1949   Culture and Ethos of Kaska Society. Yale University Publications in Anthropology 40.
Høygaard, A.
    1941   Studies on the Nutrition and Physio-Pathology of Eskimos. Skrifter Utgitt Av Det
        Norske Videnskaps-Akademi I Oslo. Mat.-Naturv. Klasse No. 9.
Hughes, J.

1960 An Epidemiological Study of Psychopathology in an Eskimo Village (Ph.D. thesis, Cornell University) Ann Arbor, Michigan: University Microfilms.

Huntington, E.
n.d. The Character of Races. New York and London.

Jochelson, W.
1908 The Koryak. *In* The Jessup North Pacific Expedition. F. Boas, Ed. Memoirs, American Museum of Natural History 6:416-417.
1926 The Yukaghir and Yukaghirized Tungus. Memoir, American Museum of Natural History. 9:30-38.

Leighton, A., and C. Hughes
1955 Notes on Eskimo Patterns of Suicide. Southwestern Journal of Anthropology 11:327-338.

MacMillan, D.
1934 How Peary Reached the Pole. Boston: Houghton Co.

Malaurie, J.
1956 The Last Kings of Thule. London: George Allen & Unwin.

Meldorf, G.
1900 Om Kajaksvimmelheden; Gronland og dens Ferhold til Brugen af Nydelsesmidler. Bibliotec for Laeger. Kobenhaven 1:524-539.

Nachman, B.
1969 Fits, Suicides, Beatings and Time-Out. Alaska Native Service. U.S.P.H.S., Anchorage, Alaska.

Novakovsky, S.
1924 Arctic or Siberian Hysteria as a Reflex of the Geographic Environment. Ecology 5:113-127.

Parker, S.
1962 Eskimo Psychopathology. American Anthropologist 64:74-96.

Peary, J.
1893 My Arctic Journal. New York: Contemporary Publishing Co.

Peary, R.
1907 Nearest the Pole. New York: Doubleday, Page.
1910 The North Pole. New York: Fredrich Stokes.

Rasmussen, K.
1927 Across Arctic America: Narrative of the Fifth Thule Expedition. New York: G. P. Putnam's Sons.
1931 The Netsilik Eskimos. Report of the Fifth Thule Expedition. Copenhagen VIII:1-542.
1932 The Intellectual Culture of the Copper Eskimo. Report of the Fifth Thule Expedition. Copenhagen IX.

Rink, H.
1875 Tales and Traditions of the Eskimos. Edinburgh & London: Wm. Blackwood & Sons.

Shackelton, E.
1939 Arctic Journeys. London: Lit. Co.

Shirokogoff, S.
1935 Psychomental Complex of the Tungus. London: Routledge and Keegan Ltd.

Spencer, R.
1959 The North Alaskan Eskimo. Bureau of American Ethnology Bulletin 171. Washington.

Steed, G.
1947 Unpublished Interviews with Niels Rasmussen. New York: International Universities Press. (Gussow, Z.: Pibloktok (Hysteria) Among the Polar Eskimo. Psychoanalytic Study of Society. Vol. 1, 1960.)

Steensby, H.
1910 Contributions to the Ethnology and Anthropogeography of the Polar Eskimo. Medelelser om Grønland.

Suicide Among Indians, Eskimos, and Aleuts in Alaska. Statistics compiled by Bureau of Indian Health, 1960-1967.

Vallee, F.
1966 Eskimo Theories of Mental Illness in the Hudson Bay Region. Anthropologica N. S. 8:53-84.

Wallace, A. F. C.
1960 An Interdisciplinary Approach to Mental Disorder Among the Polar Eskimos of Northwest Greenland. Anthropologica 11(2):1-12.
1961 Mental Illness, Biology, and Culture. *In* Psychological Anthropology. F. Hsu, Ed. Homewood, Illinois: The Dorsey Press.

Weyer, E.
1932 The Eskimos. New Haven: Yale University Press.

Whitney, H.
1911   Hunting with the Eskimo. New York: Century.
Willis, J.
1962   Mental Health in Canada's North. Ottawa, Canada: Department of Mental Health and Welfare RA 790 7-02-W734.
Willis, J., and M. Martin
1962   Mental Health in Canada's North. Ottawa, Canada: Department of Mental Health and Welfare.
Winiarz, W., and J. Weilawski
1936   Imu-a Psychoneurosis Occurring Among the Ainus. Psychoanalytic Review 23:181.
Yap, P.
1951   Mental Diseases Peculiar to Certain Cultures: A Survey of Comparative Psychiatry. Journal of Mental Science 97(407):313-327.
1952   The Latah Reaction: Its Psychodynamics and Nosological Position. Journal of Mental Science 98(413):515-562.

IV. THE EPIDEMIOLOGY OF THE ARCTIC HYSTERIAS AND OTHER MENTAL DISORDERS

Benedict, R.
1934   Patterns of Culture. New York: Houghton Mifflin.
Briggs, J.
1971   Never in Anger. Cambridge, Massachusetts: Harvard University Press.
Brody, E., Ed.
1970   Behavior in New Environment: Adaptation of Migrant Populations. Beverly Hills, California: Sage Publications.
Carpenter, E.
1953   Witch-Fear Among the Aivilik Eskimos. American Journal of Psychiatry 110:194.
Census of Population
1970   Alaska PC (IV)-3. Washington, D.C.: U.S. Department of Commerce.
Chafetz, M.
1969   Addictions: Alcoholism. In Comprehensive Textbook of Psychiatry. Freedman and Kaplan, Eds. Baltimore: Williams and Wilkins.
Comprehensive Community Mental Health Planning
1965   Alaska: Prepared by B. Ure for the Governor's Committee.
Ehrstrom, M.
1951   Medical Investigations in North Greenland 1948-1949, II. Acta Medica Scandanavia 140(IV):254-264.
Federal Field Committee for Development Planning in Alaska
1968   Alaska Natives and the Land. Washington, D.C.: U.S. Government Printing Office.
Gazaway, W.
1971   Juneau, Alaska: Compiled by the Department of Economic Resources.
Hippler, A.
1969   Patterns of Migration, Urbanization, and Acculturation. Unpublished manuscript. 20th Alaska Science Conference, University of Alaska.
International Classification of Diseases
1962   U.S. Public Health Service Publication No. 719. Washington, D.C.: U.S. Government Printing Office.
Joseph, A., and V. Murray
1951   Chammorros and Carolinians of Saipan. Cambridge, Massachusetts: Harvard University Press.
Katz, S.
1971   Biological Factors in Population Control and Their Relations to Social and Technical Change. In Population Problems and Anthropology. B. Spooner, Ed. Philadelphia: University of Pennsylvania Press.
Katz, S., and E. Foulks
1971   An Ecosystems Approach in the Arctic. Paper presented at the Second International Symposium on Circumpolar Health, Oulu, Finland.
Kroeber, A.
1952   Psychosis or Social Sanction. In The Nature of Culture. Chicago: University of Chicago Press.
Mental Disorders
1968   Washington, D.C.: American Psychiatric Association.

National Institute of Mental Health
1967 Series A, Nos. 4 and 5. Washington, D.C.: U.S. Government Printing Office.
Noyes, A., and L. Dolb
1958 Modern Clinical Psychiatry. Philadelphia: W. B. Saunders.
Parker, W.
1962 Eskimo Psychopathology. American Anthropologist 64:74-96.
Parron, H.
1954 Cited in Comprehensive Mental Health Planning 1965. Juneau, Alaska: Governors Committee.
Piers, H., and M. Singer
1953 Shame and Guilt. Springfield, Illinois: Charles C. Thomas.
Teicher, M.
1954 Three Cases of Psychosis Among the Eskimos. Journal of Mental Science 100:527-535.

V. THE ANTIQUITY OF THE NORTH ALASKAN ESKIMO: A FOUNDATION FOR THE ARCTIC HYSTERIAS

Bandi, H.
1969 Eskimo Prehistory. College, Alaska: University of Alaska Press.
Birket-Smith, K.
1959 The Eskimos. London: Methuen.
Collins, H.
1954 Comments on Time Depths of American Linguistic Groupings. American Anthropologist 56:364-372.
Dumond, D.
1965 On Eskaleution Linguistics, Archeology and Prehistory. American Anthropologist 67:1231-1253.
Ford, J.
1959 Eskimo Prehistory in the Vicinity of Point Barrow, Alaska. Anthropological Papers of the American Museum of Natural History 47:1.
Giddings, J.
1967 Ancient Men of the Arctic. New York: Alfred Knopf.
Hirsh, D.
1954 Glottochronology and Eskimo-Aleut Prehistory. American Anthropologist 56:825-838.
Holm, G.
1914 Ethnographic Sketch of the Angmagsalik Eskimo. Medelelser om Grønland 29:a-147.
Jackson, S.
1891 Introduction of Reindeer into Alaska. Preliminary Report General Agent of Education for Alaska to the Commissioner of Education, 1890.
Jenness, D.
1940 Prehistoric Culture Waves from Asia and America. Journal of Washington Academy of Sciences 30(1).
1968 Eskimo Administration: V. Analysis and Reflections. Arctic Institute of North America Technical Paper 21.
Laughlin, W.
1963 Eskimos and Aleuts, Their Origins and Evolution. Science 142:3593.
Larsen, H., and F. Rainey
1948 Ipiutak and the Arctic Whale Hunting Culture. Anthropological Papers of the American Museum of Natural History 42.
Milan, F.
1964 The Acculturation of the Contemporary Eskimo of Wainwright, Alaska. Anthropological Papers of the University of Alaska II, 2:1-97.
Oswalt, W.
1967 Alaskan Eskimos. San Francisco: Chandler Publishing Co.
Pospisil, L.
1964 Law and Societal Structure Among the Nunamiut Eskimo. *In* Explorations in Cultural Anthropology. W. Goodenough, Ed. New York: McGraw Book Co., 395-433.
Rainey, F.
1941 Eskimo Prehistory: The Okvik Site on Punuk Islands. Anthropological Papers of the American Museum of Natural History 37(Pt. 4).
Spencer, R.
1959 The North Alaskan Eskimo. Smithsonian Institution Bureau of American Ethnology, Bulletin 171.

Steensby, H.
    1917 An Anthropological Study of the Origin of the Eskimo. Medelelser om Grønland 53:39-228.
Stefansson, V.
    1914 The Stefansson-Anderson Arctic Expedition of the American Museum of Natural History: Preliminary Report. Anthropological Papers of the American Museum of Natural History 14:1.

VI. THE MATRIX OF ESKIMO CULTURE

Ackerknecht, E.
    1943 Psychopathology, Primitive Medicine and Primitive Culture. Bulletin of the History of Medicine 14.
Bogoras, W.
    n.d. The Chuckchee. *In* The Jessup North Pacific Expedition VII. F. Boas, Ed. New York: Memoir of the American Museum of Natural History.
Briggs, J.
    1971 Never in Anger. Cambridge, Massachusetts: Harvard University Press.
Chance, N.
    1966 The Eskimo of North Alaska. New York: Holt, Rinehart and Winston.
Eisenman, R.
    1965 Scapegoating and Social Control. Journal of Psychology 61:203-209.
Freud, S.
    1949 An Outline of Psychoanalysis. New York: W. W. Norton.
Gubser, N.
    1965 Nunamiut Eskimos: Hunters of Caribou. New Haven: Yale University Press.
Hartman, H.
    1958 Ego Psychology and the Problems of Adoption. New York: International Universities Press.
Hennigh, L.
    1970 Functions and Limitations of Alaskan Eskimo Wife Trading. Arctic 23(1):24-34.
Jenness, D.
    1962 Eskimo Administration: I. Alaska. Arctic Institute of North America Technical Paper No. 10.
Kris, E.
    1952 Psychoanalytic Explorations in Art. New York: International Universities Press.
Kroeber, A.
    1952 Psychosis or Social Sanction. *In* The Nature of Culture. Chicago: University of Chicago Press.
Lantis, M.
    1960 Eskimo Childhood and Interpersonal Relationships. Seattle: University of Washington Press.
Laubscher, B.
    1937 Sex, Custom and Psychopathology, A Study of South African Pagan Natives. London: Routledge & Kegan Paul Ltd.
Marsh, G.
    1954 A Comparative Survey of Eskimo-Aleut Religion. Anthropological Papers of the University of Alaska 3:21-36.
Milan, F.
    1964 The Acculturation of the Contemporary Eskimo of Wainwright, Alaska. Anthropological Papers of the University of Alaska 11(2):1-97.
Murphy, J.
    1964 Psychotherapeutic Aspects of Shamanism on St. Lawrence Island, Alaska. *In* Magic, Faith and Healing: Studies in Primitive Psychiatry Today. A. Kiev, Ed. New York: Free Press of Glencoe.
Nelson, R.
    1969 Hunters of the Northern Ice. Chicago: University of Chicago Press.
Ohlmarks, A.
    1939 Studien Zum Problem des Schamanismus. Lund: C. W. K. Gleekup.
Rasmussen, K.
    n.d. The Netsilik Eskimos. *In* Report of the Fifth Thule Expedition. Copenhagen VIII:1-542.
    1938 Posthumous Notes on the Life and Doings of the East Greenlanders in Olden Times: The Angmagsalik Eskimos. Medelelser om Grønland 101(1).
Spencer, R.
    1959 The North Alaskan Eskimo. Bureau of American Ethnology Bulletin 171.

Van Stone, J.
  1962 Point Hope. Seattle: University of Washington Press.

VII. THE ARCTIC HYSTERIAS OF THE ALASKAN INNUIT 1969-70

Gessel, A., and F. Ilg (with L. Ames and G. Bulles)
  1946 The Child from 5-10. New York: Harper and Bros.

VIII. THE CALCIUM HYPOTHESIS

Brink, F.
  1954 Role of Calcium Ion in Neural Process. Pharmacological Review 6:243.
Davidson, C.
  1963 Diseases of Nutrition. *In* Cecil-Loeb Textbook of Medicine, Vol. II. 11th Edition. P.
      Beeson and W. McDermott, Eds. Philadelphia: W. B. Saunders Co.
Denko, J., and R. Kaelbling
  1962 The Psychiatric Aspects of Hypoparathyroidism. Acta Psychiatrica Scandanavia
      164(38):1-70.
Farese, G., M. Mayer, and W. Blatt
  1970 A Membrane Ultrafiltration Procedure for Determining Diffusible Calcium in Serum.
      Clinical Chemistry 16(3):226-228.
Gronell, R., and E. Romero
  1970 The Chemistry of Thought. Medical World News February, 13:41-49.
Heller, C., and E. Scott
  1961 The Alaska Dietary Survey 1956-1961. Public Health Service Publication No. 999-AH-2.
      Washington, D.C.: U.S. Government Printing Office.
Henry, R.
  1964 Clinical Chemistry: Principles and Techniques. New York: Hoeber.
Høygaard, A.
  1941 Studies on the Nutrition and Physio-Pathology of Eskimos. Skrifter Utgitt Av Det
      Norske Videnskaps-Akademi I Oslo. Mat.-Naturv. Klasse No. 9.
Katz, S.
  1971 Serum Calcium Ion Measurements Via an Electrode: Method and Results. Unpublished
      manuscript. Philadelphia: University of Pennsylvania Press.
Katz, S., and E. Foulks
  1969 Mineral Metabolism and Behavior: Abnormalities of Calcium Homeostasis. American
      Journal of Physical Anthropology 32:229-304.
Kepner, B., and D. Hercules
  1963 Flurometric Determination of Calcium in Blood Serum. Analytic Chemistry
      35:1238-1240.
Laughlin, W.
  1970 The Purpose of Studying Eskimos and Their Population Systems. Arctic 23(1):3-13.
Mendelson, J., M. Ogata, and N. Mello
  1969 Effects of Alcohol Ingestion and Withdrawal on Magnesium States of Alcoholics: Clinical
      and Experimental Findings. Annals of the New York Academy of Sciences 162(2):918-933.
Milan, F.
  1968 The International Study of Eskimos. Arctic 21(3):123-126.
Mountcastle, V., Ed.
  1968 Medical Physiology. St. Louis: C. V. Mosby Co.
National Research Council
  1958 Food and Nutrition Board. Recommended Dietary Allowances. Publ. No. 589.
      Washington, D.C.: U.S. Government Printing Office.
Pauls, F., W. Thompson, and R. Laessig
  1969 Serological and Clinical Chemistry Patterns of Wainwright Eskimos. Paper presented at
      the A.A.A.S. 134th Annual Meeting, Boston, Massachusetts.
Phang, J. M., M. Berman, G. A. Finerman, R. M. Neer, L. E. Rosenberele, T. J. Fisher, and A.
Granger
  1969 Dietary Perturbation of Calcium Metabolism in Normal Man—Compartmental Analysis.
      Journal of Clinical Investigation 48:67-79.
Rasmussen, H., and M. Pechet
  1970 Calcitonin. Scientific American October:42-50.
Stefansson
  1945 My Life with the Eskimo. New York: Collier.

Wallace, A. F. C.
  1961 Mental Health, Biology and Culture. *In* Psychological Anthropology. F. Hsu, Ed. Homewood, Illinois: Dorsey Press.
Wintrobe, M., G. Thorn, R. Adams, I. Bennett, E. Brunwald, K. Isselbacker, and R. Petersderf, Eds.
  1970 Harrison's Principles of Internal Medicine. 6th Edition. New York: McGraw-Hill.

IX. CALCIUM RHYTHMS

Bohlen, J.
  1970 Circadian and Circannual Rhythms in Eskimos. Unpublished manuscript. University of Wisconsin, Madison.
Bohlen, J., F. Milan, and F. Halberg
  1970 Circumpolar Chronobiology. Proceedings of the Ninth International Congress of Anatomists, Leningrad.
Halberg, F.
  1969 Chronobiology. Annual Review of Physiology 31:675-725.
Luce, G.
  1970 Biological Rhythms in Psychiatry and Medicine. Public Health Service Publication No. 2088.
Reimann, H.
  1963 Periodic Disease. Oxford, England: Blackwell Scientific Publications.

X. ARCTIC HYSTERIA AND DISORDERS OF THE CENTRAL NERVOUS SYSTEM

Altshuler, K.
  1969 Deafness and Schizophrenia. Psychiatric News September: 8.
Brody, J., T. Overfield, and R. McAlister
  1965 Draining Ears and Deafness Among Alaskan Eskimos. Archives of Otolaryngology 81:29-33.
Davidson, C.
  1963 Diseases of Nutrition. *In* Cecil-Loeb Textbook of Medicine Vol. II. Eleventh Edition. P. Beeson and W. McDermott, Eds. Philadelphia: W. B. Saunders.
Environmental Epilepsy Rises.
  1971 Medical World News 12(29):17-21.
Ervin, F.
  1967 Brain Disorders: Associated with Convulsions (Epilepsy). *In* Comprehensive Textbook of Psychiatry. A. Freedman and H. Kaplan, Eds. Baltimore: Williams and Wilkins.
Fortiune, R.
  1968 The Health of the Eskimos, as Portrayed in the Early Accounts of Explorers, Traders, and Missionaries. Unpublished manuscript. University of Alaska, Fairbanks.
Hopkins, H.
  1965 Leopold's Principles and Methods of Physical Diagnosis. Philadelphia: W. B. Saunders.
Lennox, W.
  1960 Epilepsy and Related Disorders I. Boston: Little, Brown & Co.
Merritt, H.
  1967 A Textbook of Neurology. Philadelphia: Sea and Febiger.
Maynard, J.
  1969 Otitis Media in Alaskan Eskimo Children: An Epidemiologic Review with Observations in Control. Alaska Medicine 11(3):93-97.
Noyes, A., and L. Kolb
  1959 Modern Clinical Psychiatry. 5th Edition. Philadelphia: W. B. Saunders.
Oshinsky, L.
  1964 The Most Ancient Eskimos. The Canadian Research Center for Anthropology.
Reed, D., S. Struve, and J. Maynard
  1967 Otitis Media and Hearing Deficiency Among Eskimo Children: A Cohort Study. American Journal of Public Health 57(9):1657-1662.
Valle, B.
  1958 Metals and Metabolism. *In* Principles of Internal Medicine. 3rd Edition. T. Harrison, R. Adams, I. Bennett, W. Resnik, G. Thorn, and M. Wintrobs, Eds. New York: McGraw-Hill.
Veith, I.
  1965 Hysteria, The History of a Disease. Chicago: University of Chicago Press.

Wallace, A. F. C.
    1960 An Interdisciplinary Approach to Mental Disorder Among the Polar Eskimos of Northwest Greenland. Anthropologica N.S. 11(2):1-12.

XI. THE PSYCHOLOGY OF THE ARCTIC HYSTERIAS

Benedict, R.
    1946 The Chrysanthemum and the Sword. Boston: Houghton Mifflin. pp. 222-224.
Blos, P.
    1962 On Adolescence: A Psychoanalytic Interpretation. New York: Free Press of Glencoe.
Chance, N.
    1965 Acculturation, Self-Identification, and Personality Adjustment. American Anthropologist 67:372-373.
Clairmont, D.
    1963 Divorce Among Indians and Eskimos in Aklavik. Ottawa: Department of Northern Affairs and Natural Resources.
Erikson, E.
    1950 Childhood and Society. New York: W. W. Norton & Co.
Lynd, H.
    1961 On Shame and the Search for Identity. New York: Science Editions, Inc.
Mead, M.
    1970 Culture and Commitment: A Study of the Generation Gap. Garden City: Natural History Press.
Piers, G., and M. Singer
    1953 Shame and Guilt. Springfield, Illinois: Charles C. Thomas.
Vallee, F.
    1968 Stresses of Change and Mental Health Among the Canadian Eskimos. Archives of Environmental Health 17:565-570.

XII. A SYNTHESIS

Bloom, J.
    1972 Population Trends of Alaskan Natives and the Need for Planning. American Journal of Psychiatry 128(8):112-116.
Erikson, E.
    1950 Childhood and Society. New York: W. W. Norton & Co.
Hippler, A.
    1968 Some Unplanned Consequences of Planned Culture Change. University of Alaska Institute of Social, Economic and Government Research.
Jenness, D.
    1968 Eskimo Administration: V. Analysis and Reflections. Arctic Institute of North America Technical Paper No. 21.
Kroeber, A.
    1963 Anthropology: Culture Patterns and Processes. New York: Harcourt, Brace & World.
Lowie, R.
    1937 The History of Ethnological Theory. New York.
Mack-Brunswick, R.
    n.d. The Pre-Oedipal Phase of the Libido Development.
Mead, M.
    1970 Culture and Commitment: A Study of the Generation Gap. Garden City: Natural History Press.
Opler, M.
    1967 Culture and Social Psychiatry. New York: Atherton.
Speck, R., J. Barr, R. Eisenmann, A. Goldman, E. Foulks, and J. Lincoln
    1972 The New Families. New York: Basic Books.
Toffler, A.
    1970 Future Shock. New York: Random House.

Index